The Observer Book of
THE EARTH

Editor
Carl Wilkinson

Contributors
Professor Michael Benton; Killian Fox; Bob Gatliff; Dr James Lovelock;
Dr Robert Macfarlane; Robin McKie; Dave Nixon; George Pendle;
Miguel Rodriguez; Fiona Spence; Neil Spencer; Dr Iain Stewart; Tom Templeton;
Professor Stanley Williams; Gordon Wright; Dr Jan Zalasiewicz

Observer Books
Lisa Darnell

Sub-editor
Leah Jewett

Researchers
James Fulker, Tessa Harris

Executive editor
Robert Yates

First published by Observer Books 2008
Observer Books is an imprint of Guardian News and Media

Printed and bound in the UK by Cox & Wyman Ltd, Reading, Berkshire

Pictures: Bettmann/Corbis, Alamy, Hulton Archive/Getty Images, Corbis,
AAA Collection, Science Photo Library, Mary Evans Picture Library,
Ordinance Survey, AP

Cover design: Two Associates
Text design: seagulls.net
Graphics: Cath Levett
Picture research: Alicia Canter

The Observer Book of the Earth is the 10th book in the current series. Previous titles are
Genius, Weather, Film, Scandal, Money, Rock & Pop, Space, The Body and Food

Introduction

'Once a photograph of the Earth, taken from outside, is available – once the sheer isolation of the Earth becomes known,' the British astronomer Sir Fred Hoyle once said, 'a new idea as powerful as any in history will be let loose.'

He was right. Those great 19th- and 20th-century ideals of science and curiosity have transformed our understanding of the Earth to the point where we think nothing of viewing its surface via satellites from computers in our homes, zooming in on geographical features at will. Although mankind's time on Earth has been short (famously, if the entire lifespan of the planet so far were compressed into a 24-hour day, our time would amount to mere seconds), our understanding of this glorious iridescent pearl hanging in a vast dark ocean of space has exploded. We have measured, tested, sampled, drilled and climbed almost everything we can get our hands on. And we are remoulding the landscape faster than it has ever been changed before.

In this book, we explore our planet, getting under its skin by talking to everyone from geologists to miners, oceanographers and water diviners. We uncover how mountains are created, how glaciers work and how volcanos – such as the one in Hawaii shown on the cover – can tear open the Earth. We consider how our views of the landscapes which surround us have metamorphosed, investigate the impact a changing climate will have on the Earth as we know it today, and travel back into the distant past to discover ancient continents that formed and split even before dinosaurs roamed the Earth. Along the way, we learn how to choose diamonds, hunt for fossils and measure the height of the world's tallest mountains.

Welcome to *The Observer Book of the Earth*.

A–Z of the Earth

A **Archipelago** An often volcanic chain or cluster of islands. Japan, the Philippines, New Zealand, Indonesia and the UK are the largest states that are mainly archipelagos.

B **Bedrock** The solid rock beneath any soil, sediment or other surface cover. In some places it may be exposed at the Earth's surface.

C **Core** The extremely dense centre of the Earth, which is believed to be comprised of a solid inner core and a liquid outer core, both made up of pure metals such as iron and nickel and with a temperature of around 3,500C.

D **Delta** A sedimentary deposit that forms where a stream or river enters a standing body of water such as a lake or ocean. The name is derived from the Greek letter delta because these deposits typically have a triangular shape when viewed from above.

E **Erosion** The process by which earth and rock are worn away by gravity, wind, water and ice.

F **Fault** A fracture or fracture zone in rock along which movement has occurred.

G **Geyser** A hot spring that periodically erupts, spraying a column of steam and hot water into the air. The word derives from the Icelandic word *gjósa*, meaning 'to erupt'.

H **Hanging valleys** Small valleys cut by tributary glaciers which have not carved as deeply as the main glaciers they feed. When the ice melts, these small valleys are left 'hanging' above the main trough and often feature waterfalls.

I **Igneous** The Earth's primary rock, which forms when molten material cools on the surface, at a shallow depth or deep underground.

L **Lithosphere** The solid, rocky outer part of the Earth approximately 50 miles thick comprising the crust and the solid portion of the mantle (the zone between the crust and the core).

M **Metamorphic** A form of rock derived from either sedimentary or igneous rocks transformed by extreme pressure and temperature over millions of years.

N **Nunatak** An Inuit word for land and mountains which are surrounded by glacial ice.

O **Orogenesis** The formation of mountains by volcanism, plate collision, folding or the movement of fault blocks.

P **Plate tectonics** The geological model in which the Earth's lithosphere is divided into a number of more or less rigid segments which move in relation to one another, often causing seismic activity where the plates meet.

Q **Quaternary** The period of Earth's history from about 2 million years ago to the present. The word is also used to describe the rock and deposits of this time span.

R **Ring of Fire** The term used to describe the regions of mountain-building volcanos which surround the Pacific Ocean.

S **Sedimentary** Crushed rock and organic material often laid down underwater and compacted to form new rock. It often includes fossils produced from the organic matter of plants and animals.

T **Tsunami** A great sea wave produced by a submarine earthquake, volcanic eruption or large landslide into the ocean.

U **Uniformitarianism** The theory that current geological processes such as erosion, weathering and the movement of plates have been occurring throughout the Earth's history and explain previous geological events.

V **Vulcan** Roman god of fire who gave his name to volcanos.

W **Weathering** The physical, chemical and biological processes by which rock is broken down into smaller pieces. It can occur as water dissolves soluble rock such as limestone; as water in cracks freezes, forcing them apart; or as roots break up rock, turning it into soil.

X **Xenolith** A large body of rock embedded in newer igneous rock. It is formed when rising magma surrounds pre-existing rock but does not melt it.

Y **Yield point** The maximum amount of stress that rock can withstand without being permanently deformed. Under substantial pressure and heat, rock can bend, crack or metamorphose.

Z **Zircon** An often colourless mineral deposit, zirconium silicate is used as a diamond substitute since it has a lustre and appearance similar to those of the more expensive stone. It is also found with blue, violet, green, brown, red or yellow tints.

Earth timeline

» 4,700 million years ago (mya)
Our solar system and the Earth form from a ball of gas and dust. The **Moon** is thought to have been created from the **Earth** when it was sideswiped by a massive body around the same size as **Mars**, which sent a chunk of crust into orbit

» 4,550mya
Precambrian era begins

» 1,850my
A meteor impact i Sudbury in Ontari Canada leaves a 250km-wide crate

4,500   3,500   2,500

» 3,500mya
Traces of **life** have been found in rocks dating back to around this time in the **Archean eon**

» 3,000mya
The make-up of the atmosphere is around **75% nitrogen, 15% carbon dioxide**. Meanwhile, the **Sun** brightens to around 80% of its current level

» 2,000m
Solar luminosity reaches 85% of its current level

» 33.9mya
Oligocene epoch. Alpine evolution during this time of major **mountain-building**

» 160,000 years ago
Homo sapiens appear

PRESENT   25   50

» 11,000 years ago
The end of the last major **glacial epoch** causes sea levels to rise by around 91m (300ft)

» 1.64mya-present
Quaternary period. The **northern hemisphere** is greatly affected by ice ages

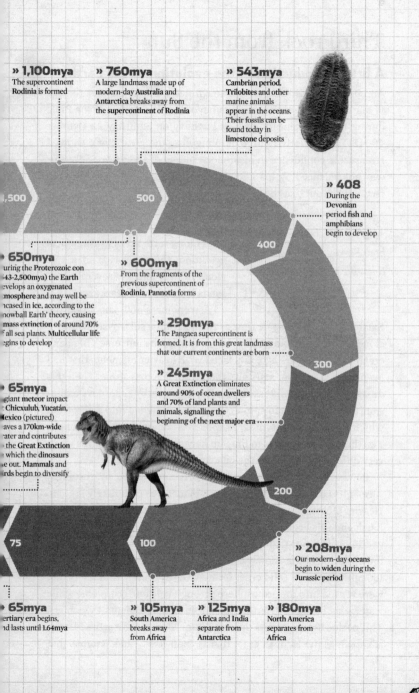

» 1,100mya
The supercontinent **Rodinia** is formed

» 760mya
A large landmass made up of modern-day **Australia** and **Antarctica** breaks away from the **supercontinent** of Rodinia

» 543mya
Cambrian period.
Trilobites and other marine animals appear in the oceans. Their fossils can be found today in **limestone** deposits

» 408
During the **Devonian** period **fish** and amphibians begin to develop

● 650mya
...uring the Proterozoic eon (...43-2,500mya) the **Earth** ...evelops an oxygenated ...mosphere and may well be ...ncased in ice, according to the ...nowball Earth' theory, causing ...mass extinction of around 70% ...f all sea plants. **Multicellular life** ...egins to develop

» 600mya
From the fragments of the previous supercontinent of **Rodinia, Pannotia** forms

» 290mya
The Pangaea supercontinent is formed. It is from this great landmass that our current continents are born ·····

» 245mya
A **Great Extinction** eliminates around 90% of ocean dwellers and 70% of land plants and animals, signalling the beginning of the next major era ·······

● 65mya
...giant meteor impact ...t Chicxulub, Yucatán, ...Mexico (pictured) ...aves a 170km-wide ...rater and contributes ...the Great Extinction ...n which the dinosaurs ...e out. Mammals and ...irds begin to diversify

» 208mya
Our modern-day **oceans** begin to **widen** during the **Jurassic** period

● 65mya
...ertiary era begins, ...nd lasts until 1.64mya

» 105mya
South America breaks away from **Africa**

» 125mya
Africa and India separate from **Antarctica**

» 180mya
North America separates from **Africa**

1,500   500   400   300   200

75   100

Third rock from the Sun

A brief introduction to the evolution of the Earth

Archbishop James Ussher of Armagh had no doubts about the age of our planet. The Earth, he calculated from his studies of the Bible during the 17th century, had its birthday on Saturday 22 October 4004BC at precisely 6pm. If nothing else, the good cleric showed remarkable confidence in his understanding of scripture. Sadly, this was not balanced by his knowledge of geology and astronomy. In fact, it turns out that the world we inhabit is 4.6 billion years old. Far from being the recent handiwork of a deity, the Earth is the outcome of a very long-term act of astronomical evolution: the coalescing of a vast cloud of dust and gas several thousands of millions of years ago.

> 66 *What's the use of a fine house if you haven't got a tolerable planet to put it on?*
> Henry David Thoreau

Astronomers now know that the Earth formed at the same time as the rest of the solar system. First a cloud of hydrogen and helium, left over from the universe's Big Bang creation 13.7bn years ago, was laced with heavier elements that had been created in other stars and then wafted across space. Then this dusty cloud was compressed, possibly by a nearby supernova explosion, and slow began to spin. As a result it flattened into a disk from which a central Sun formed, as well as a family of orbiting planets. The third-closest planet to the Sun became Earth, though this was a very different world from the one we know today.

Bombarded by interplanetary debris and heated by the pressure of its contraction, the newborn planet was completely molten. Heavier elements, including iron, sank to form the core of the early Earth and this began to generate a magnetic field which has continued to protect our planet's atmosphere ever since – a key factor in the evolution of life. Slowly the Earth cooled, and after about 100 to 150 million years a solid crust formed. Gases from within the planet were vented into the atmosphere through volcanic eruptions, while water was brought to Earth thanks to bombardments by comets. This period, which covers the first 500m years of the Earth's history, is known as the Hadean era – that is, 'hell-like' – and assumes that conditions were fiery and hot throughout our planet's infancy. Recently, however, some scientists have argued that temperatures were actually much lower and that the Earth's oceans – initially thought to have formed about 750m years – appeared much earlier, indeed almost as soon as the planet formed.

Either way, the Earth was very unlike the one we know today. Scientists calculate that its atmosphere contained ammonia, methane, carbon dioxide and nitrogen. There would have been no free oxygen. Adding to this grimly inhospitably environment, the Earth – lacking any protective ozone layer – would have been pounded by ultraviolet radiation from the Sun. Slowly changes accrued, however, and chemicals coalesced until – around 3.5bn years ago – the first simple living organisms appeared.

At the same time, the first continents assembled, followed not long afterwards by the creation of the first titanic landmass, or supercontinent. Since then a series of supercontinents have formed and then broken up in response to the movement of the tectonic plates on which the Earth's crust rests. These plates – there are seven major and many minor ones – account for the current positions of the continents, their movements over geological time, and many of the volcanic eruptions, earthquakes, and tsunamis that afflict our planet. Sometimes a plate moves apart from its neighbour. Magma from below bubbles up and volcanic eruptions ensue. On other occasions, two plates collide, triggering earthquakes. In short, we live on an active world. The benefits are our grand mountain ranges, canyons and other geological wonders. The perils come with those occasional eruptions and tsunamis.

Most importantly the Earth's geology, although active, was not too destructive, however, and provided stability for most of the past 4.6bn years – enough to ensure not only the appearance of life but also its evolution into increasingly complex forms, including one group of promising early developers: Homo sapiens. **Robin McKie**

Robin McKie is the science editor for The Observer

> 66 *Don't go around saying the world owes you a living. The world owes you nothing. It was here first.*
>
> Mark Twain

A beginner's guide to the Earth

Circumference

The circumference of the Earth at the equator is 24,901.55 miles (40,075.16km), but measured through the poles it is 24,859.82 miles (40,008km), meaning that there is a slight bulge at the equator. The Earth's shape is therefore not a perfect sphere, but actually an oblate spheroid, or geoid

Axis

The Earth's rotation is not perfect – there is in fact a slight 'wobble' as the axis is tilted at around 23.44 degrees off its orbital plane. This means that over the course of a year the northern hemisphere will be closer to the Sun for part of the year than it is during the other part of the year. This tilt is the main cause for the Earth's seasons. The wobble comes in because on a 41,000-year cycle the tilt varies between 22.1 and 24.5 degrees

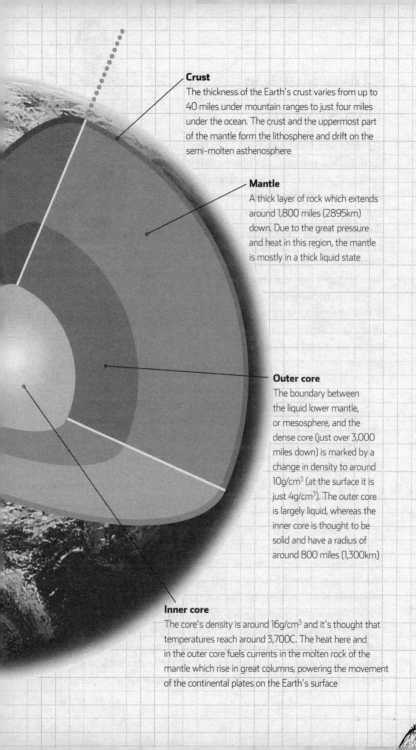

Crust
The thickness of the Earth's crust varies from up to 40 miles under mountain ranges to just four miles under the ocean. The crust and the uppermost part of the mantle form the lithosphere and drift on the semi-molten asthenosphere

Mantle
A thick layer of rock which extends around 1,800 miles (2895km) down. Due to the great pressure and heat in this region, the mantle is mostly in a thick liquid state

Outer core
The boundary between the liquid lower mantle, or mesosphere, and the dense core (just over 3,000 miles down) is marked by a change in density to around $10g/cm^3$ (at the surface it is just $4g/cm^3$). The outer core is largely liquid, whereas the inner core is thought to be solid and have a radius of around 800 miles (1,300km)

Inner core
The core's density is around $16g/cm^3$ and it's thought that temperatures reach around 3,700C. The heat here and in the outer core fuels currents in the molten rock of the mantle which rise in great columns, powering the movement of the continental plates on the Earth's surface

Iain Stewart

My main interest is in hazards – I'm fascinated by earthquakes, volcanos and plate tectonics. Studying them presents the opportunity to perhaps help with some of the problems that natural disasters can cause, and also offers us a window into how the Earth works. So you might not just be interested in looking at a volcano because it could destroy a town – you'll also want to know what it tells us about processes deep within the Earth. It's that dichotomy which I really enjoy.

One of the aspects of geology that is as frustrating as it is intriguing is that you only ever get a very partial view. You're looking at rocks that are completely weird because they're on the Earth's surface. Rocks are meant to be underground, under pressure – instead you're looking at this thin coating of rock that's completely different to what's down there, and you have to use this patchy evidence to get an idea of the big picture. You have to do mental leaps all the time, to extrapolate. The temptation with all science is to say: 'We need more data' and so you fill in the gaps in between – but I think with geologists more than anyone else you're forced to say: 'Given that we know that... let's take a guess.' You have to accept that you're getting incomplete information, and part of the scientific methodology of geology is guesswork – it's like being a geological detective.

And there are still some big unanswered questions. We still don't really understand the mass biota extinctions, such as the one 251 million years ago when 90% of life was wiped out. That's still up for grabs. Even the great K-T impact (the meteor that struck near the Mexican coast 65m years ago) which supposedly wiped out the dinosaurs is still something of a mystery, as we now know that these extinctions were happening before the impact.

Something that's come out over the past few years, which is pertinent to the whole climate-change debate going on now, is the importance of methane. As a greenhouse gas it's 23 times stronger than carbon dioxide, and so every time it's been released into the atmosphere we've seen evidence of warming. Methane's being used as a 'smoking gun' in many of the new theories surrounding past extinctions, but we've got no example of how that works – it's all theoretical. Terrifyingly, there's a vast methane pocket under Siberia locked into the frozen soil. It's always trickled out, but the low temperatures of the permafrost have ensured that most of it has stayed buried. Global warming could make this permafrost melt and release the methane, which will immediately produce a massive rise in global temperatures, which will warm the frost more, releasing more methane. A lot of quite frightening climate models haven't even included methane, so when it is added, these predictions suddenly become apocalyptic.

The really fundamental questions we're going to be asking about the Earth will surround population rise and the demand for natural resources. Climate change will definitely affect the amount of resources available, but the key problem we'll face in the 21st century is that more people are going to be fighting for a dwindling amount of land and resources. The social changes this is likely to bring about are massive: mass migration, global conflict and so on. Those who say it's just going to make southern England a nicer place for a holiday are being naive. There are some very scary statistics involving the fact that if you have earthquakes and volcanos just going off at their normal rate, and if we continue to build mega-cities in places where it might not be safe to do so, we could start seeing 1m to 3m death tolls.

What's nice about any scientific subject, but particularly geology because there are so many unknowns, is that the ideas we now hold dear may be laughable in 50 years' time, while things that we now think of as total fallacies could be proved right. You can be sure that 20% of what I'm teaching my students now, maybe more, will be total rubbish 20 years from now. That's why I don't want them focusing on facts and figures – these can all change – but instead on critical thinking.

I think it's a really good time in geology; since the Sixties it's come alive. Plate tectonics opened up a whole new world of theories, then space technology gave us the chance to prove them. Geography makes you feel as if you're part of one great natural system. **DR IAIN STEWART**

Dr Iain Stewart is a lecturer in geology at the University of Plymouth and presented the BBC documentary Earth: The Power of the Planet

Living on the edge

The Flat Earth myth

Despite what the ever-confused members of the worryingly popular Flat Earth Society may have you believe, the vast majority of people, churchgoing or not, have known that the Earth is a sphere for more than 2,000 years.

Eratosthenes came up with a startlingly close estimation of the Earth's circumference (around 250,000 miles) in the 3rd century BC, while Strabo and Ptolemy's less accurate approximation of 180,000 miles was widely known throughout the medieval world. Christopher Columbus, far from trying to convince a naive and backward Catholic Church that the Earth was round, was, by undertaking his voyage to India, attempting to convince the learned scientific elite that Ptolemy's figure was indeed correct. In the end, it was Columbus who was proved wrong, as the extra 70,000 miles unaccounted for in Ptolemy's calculation was filled with the bounties of the New World and the depths of the Pacific.

> 66 *The Church says the Earth is flat, but I know that it is round, for I have seen the shadow on the Moon, and I have more faith in a shadow than in the Church.*
>
> Ferdinand Magellan

So how did the Flat Earth myth come about? The first accounts of a widespread medieval belief in a flat Earth appear in the early 19th century. The American author Washington Irving, in the fictional *The Life and Voyages of Christopher Columbus*, attempted to spice up Columbus' story by portraying him as a noble visionary standing up to a church that believed the Earth was 'flat like a plate'. The idea quickly spread among the growing secular movement, which saw it as a formidable weapon in the increasingly hostile war between science and religion – any religious denier of ultramodern theories such as evolution and an ancient Earth could swiftly be shamed by a reference to their Catholic predecessors' rejection of an idea as simple as a spherical Earth.

Atlas (first representations c900BC)

Greek mythology tells of Atlas (pictured), a mighty Titan who fought the Olympian gods during the great Titanomachy war. After the Titans' defeat, Atlas was punished by Zeus, who condemned the great giant to stand at the edge of the Earth and hold up the sky for eternity.

The turtle/elephant theory (first Vedic folklore dates back to c1500BC)

Hindu folklore has it that the Earth is held up by four huge elephants standing on top of a turtle. What holds up the turtle? The infamous quote Stephen Hawking mentions in his introduction to *A Brief History of Time* asserts: 'It's turtles all the way down.'

Expanding Earth (1889)

As we entered the age of science, wild theories explaining the unexplainable were still as popular as ever. Before the theory of plate tectonics showed how the modern Earth came to be, many geologists explained the separation of the ancient supercontinents into modern landmasses by claiming that the Earth was once a tiny ball which has expanded over time. Some scientists still tenuously cling to the outdated theory; the vast majority don't.

Hydroplate Earth (1995)

Walt Brown, director of the Center for Scientific Creation, claims to have come up with irrefutable evidence that beneath the Earth's crust lay a massive reservoir of water, which spilled onto the Earth as Noah's flood and formed the planet's surface as we know it. Creationists rejoiced; scientists quickly dismissed this outré idea.

Eratosthenes of Cyrene

(b. c275BC; d. c195BC)
Greek polymath

Known as the father of geography – a word he is thought to have coined – Eratosthenes, who was born in modern-day Libya, was the first to give an accurate figure for the circumference of the Earth, using just a stick, the Sun and basic geometry. This impressive feat brought him lasting fame. Meanwhile his *Geographica* (literally 'Earth writing') introduced the climatic concepts of torrid, temperate and frigid zones, as well as debunking the common Greek myth that only a narrow belt of the Earth was habitable.

Despite these considerable accomplishments, Eratosthenes was teased throughout his life with the nickname Beta (as opposed to alpha), as it was thought that he spread himself across so many subjects that he could never be the best at any of them. It's not hard to see why: at various times he was an eminent historian, a respected poet and an imperious mathematician, and for more than 20 years he worked as the chief librarian at the Library of Alexandria – the greatest library of the time, with more than 700,000 papyrus scrolls.

It was while working there that his fascination with geography led him to create the first maps based on meridians of longitude and parallels of latitude. However, he realised he had one major problem: scale. Without knowing how big the Earth was, there was no way he could create an accurate picture of the world, and so he devised an ingenious scheme to measure it. Knowing that the Earth is spherical, he reasoned that the angle between a stick and its shadow at noon on the summer solstice – a time at which he knew the Sun was directly over the town of Cyrene, 500 miles from Alexandria – would be the same as how far round the Earth, in degrees, Alexandria was from Cyrene. By combining this figure and the rough distance in *stades* (a Greek unit of measurement, equal to about ¹⁄₁₀th of a mile) between the two cities, Eratosthenes calculated that the Earth's circumference was 25,000 miles. Today we know it is 24,901 miles.

In the beginning...

The creation of the Earth according to the Bible

The first day In the beginning God created the heavens and the Earth. Now the Earth was formless and empty, darkness was over the surface of the deep, and the Spirit of God was hovering over the waters. And God said, 'Let there be light', and there was light.

The second day And God said, 'Let there be an expanse between the waters to separate water from water.' So God made the expanse and separated the water under the expanse from the water above it. And it was so. God called the expanse 'sky'. And there was evening, and there was morning.

The third day And God said, 'Let the water under the sky be gathered to one place, and let dry ground appear.' And it was so. God called the dry ground 'land', and the gathered waters he called 'seas'.

The fourth day And God said, 'Let there be lights in the expanse of the sky to separate the day from the night, and let them serve as signs to mark seasons and days and years, and let them be lights in the expanse of the sky to give light on the Earth.' And it was so.

The fifth day And God said, 'Let the water teem with living creatures, and let birds fly above the Earth across the expanse of the sky.'

The sixth day Then God said, 'Let us make man in our image, in our likeness, and let them rule over the fish of the sea and the birds of the air, over the livestock, over all the Earth, and over all the creatures that move along the ground.' So God created man in his own image, in

the image of God he created him; male and female he created them. ... God saw all that he had made, and it was very good. And there was evening, and there was morning. Thus the heavens and the Earth were completed in all their vast array.

The seventh day God had finished the work he had been doing; so on the seventh day he rested from all his work.

Taken from the Book of Genesis, chapters 1-2

The dawn of time

Eight myths surrounding the Earth's creation

1 Greek The great goddess of the Ancient Greeks, Gaia represented the Earth. She appeared out of Chaos, the primordial void of emptiness within the universe which preceded all life. And from Gaia, or Mother Earth, sprang the sky, personified as the god Uranus (and Gaia's husband), and the mountains, plains, seas and rivers.

2 Egyptian Geb was worshipped at the city of Heliopolis in Lower Egypt as the god of Earth. Depicted as a bearded man with a goose on his head, he was the provider of crops and a healer. It was thought that his laughter caused earthquakes. Legend has it that Geb married his sister Nut, the sky goddess, angering the powerful Sun god Re, who forced their father Shu – the god of air – to separate them, thus dividing the Earth from the sky.

3 Mayan The Mayans believed that the Earth was flat, with four corners representing the cardinal points and signalled by different colours: white for north, yellow for south, red for east, black for west, and green at the centre. At each corner sat a jaguar called a *bacab* supporting the heavens. Mayans also believed that the universe was divided into layers, each containing only one celestial body. Heaven was formed of 13 layers, and the underworld of nine layers, with nine corresponding lords of the night. The Sun and Moon passed through the Earth when they disappeared below the horizon, and during his night journey beneath the Earth, the Sun became the fearsome god of the underworld, Kinich Ahau.

4 Aztec Coatlicue (meaning Serpent Skirt), the goddess of life and death, was depicted as a woman with sharp claws, a skirt of snakes and a necklace of hearts torn from sacrificial victims. Her husband Mixcoatl was the cloud serpent and god of the chase. Coatlicue gave birth to Huitzilopochtli after being mysteriously touched by a ball of feathers. This shameful pregnancy offended her other 400 children who, led by her daughter Coyolxauhqui (or Golden Bells), resolved to kill Coatlicue. However, Huitzilopochtli leapt fully armed from Coatlicue's womb and slaughtered his siblings, cutting off the head of his sister and throwing it into the sky, where it became the Moon.

5 Maori According to the New Zealand Maoris, at the beginning of time Rangi (the Sky Father) and Papa (Mother Earth) were entwined in a close embrace, trapping several of their offspring. These gods tried in vain to separate their parents, and were about to kill them until Tane, the god of forests, intervened and split his parents by pushing away his father with his head and his mother with his feet. Once separated, the sky and the Earth assumed their present position, but the storm god Tawhiri, upset with Tane, created storms and hurricanes to ravage the forests and establish his authority over the sky and his siblings. The god of war, Tu, did not want to submit to the storm god, and the struggle between Tu and Tawhiri – representing the beginning of warfare – created the islands of the Pacific Ocean.

6 Incan The ancient Peruvians believed that Pachamama personified the Earth and her husband, Inti, the Sun. They were viewed as generous deities, and llamas and other animals were offered as sacrifices to them. Pachamama continues to be worshipped today in Peru, where Christians have identified her with the Virgin Mary.

7 Norse Midgard (the Middle Earth) was created from the flesh of the primeval giant Ymir. The supreme god Odin and his brothers Vili and Ve slayed the giant and formed the ocean from his blood and sweat, the mountains and stones from his bones and teeth, the sky from his skull (supported by four dwarfs) and the clouds from his brain. The first man and woman were then carved from Ymir's left armpit.

8 Sumerian The Sumerians lived more than 3,000 years ago in Mesopotamia, which corresponds to the valleys of the Tigris and Euphrates rivers – today part of Iraq. The god of Earth and air, Enlil, was generated by the union of An, the personification of heaven, and Ki, who represents the Earth. Enlil was banished to the world of the dead for raping the grain goddess Ninlil. She followed him to the underworld to give birth to the Moon god, Sin, but Enlil and Ninlil had to sacrifice their next three children in order for Sin to rise and light up the night sky.

The magnificent seven

Natural wonders of the world

In 200BC, Philon of Byzantium chose to celebrate seven great man-made monuments including the Colossus of Rhodes, the Great Pyramid at Giza and the hanging gardens of Babylon – a list that became known as the Seven Wonders. Here are seven natural wonders...

1 Grand Canyon, USA

It has taken millions of years of erosion to form the deep, steep-sided canyon which snakes across Arizona. A mile down runs the Colorado River, and to descend into the canyon is to travel through almost half the Earth's lifespan recorded in the layers of rock. The first European to set eyes on the stunning formation was Spanish explorer García López de Cárdenas in 1540. In search of fabled lost cities of gold, he returned to Mexico thwarted in his travels by the impassable canyon. The Grand Canyon National Park was established in 1919 and became a magnet for tourists: today it attracts about 5 million visitors annually.

2 Great Barrier Reef, Australia

Discovered by Captain James Cook when he ran aground on it in the Endeavour in 1770, the 1,242 mile (2,000km) long reef tracks around the northeast coast of Australia, in places just 30 miles off shore, and is made up of the skeletons of marine polyps. Although it is the world's longest natural wonder and covers around 137,600 square miles (344,000 sq km), the Great Barrier Reef is incredibly fragile and susceptible to pollution and slight changes in sea temperature.

3 Harbour of Rio de Janeiro, Brazil

A great granite peak that has stood unmoved in the face of the erosion which has stripped the gneisses (metamorphic rocks) that surrounded it, the 1,325ft-high Sugar Loaf Mountain dominates the stunning Guanabara Bay. It was discovered by Portuguese navigators on 1 January 1502 – hence the name Rio de Janeiro, or January River.

4 Mount Everest, Nepal

When the Indian subcontinent collided with Asia around 60m years ago, the rock of the two continental plates crumpled, producing the highest mountain range in the world – the Himalayas (meaning 'abode of snow' in Sanskrit). The tallest of the Himalayan peaks is Everest, which is more than 29,000ft (8,800m) high. It was first successfully summited on 29 May 1953 by New Zealand climber Sir Edmund Hillary and the Sherpa Tenzing Norgay.

5 Northern Lights (Aurora Borealis), North Pole

Caused by charged particles in the solar wind interacting with the Earth's magnetic field, the Aurora Borealis (Aurora was the Roman goddess of dawn, *borealis* the Greek word for north wind) is a 'curtain' of green and red light emissions from sheets of falling electrons seen near the north pole primarily from September to October and March to April. In the south it is known as the Aurora Australis.

6 Paricutin Volcano, Mexico

In 1943 in a cornfield 200 miles west of Mexico City, a volcano burst forth from the Earth and within a year had reached a height of 1,100ft (335m). A year later it had buried the town of Paricutin. The new volcano eventually covered around 10 square miles by the time the eruption ended in 1952, leaving a cone 1,390ft high.

7 Victoria Falls, Zambia

The Zambezi River – the fourth-longest in Africa – rolls through Angola, Zambia and Mozambique before spilling out into the Indian Ocean. Along the way it tumbles over the world's largest and most spectacular waterfall – the 328ft (100m) high and 1.2 mile (2km) wide Victoria Falls. The falls mark a fault in the great basalt basin that forms the bed of the Zambezi. First seen by an outsider in 1855 when Scottish missionary David Livingstone arrived and named them for the British queen, the falls were known to local tribes as Mosi-oa-Tunya (or the Smoke That Thunders).

Islands of the mind

The story of the lost island of Atlantis

According to Plato in his *Timaeus* and *Critias* dialogues (written c360BC), 9,000 years earlier a great island, 'larger than Libya (Africa) and Asia together', sat in the Atlantic Ocean past the Pillars of Hercules (thought to be the 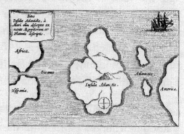 Strait of Gibraltar). From here the Atlantians (named after their first king, the titan Atlas) launched a huge military expedition eastward into the Mediterranean and were unstoppable until they came up against the Athenians. They were banished and subsequently punished by the gods for their warring ways with apocalyptic earthquakes and floods, until their ravaged island sank beneath the waves.

The veracity of the story is dubious – it is far more likely to be a parable explaining why empires such as Atlantis are doomed to fail (Plato described the island as a corrupt oligarchy, the opposite of the ideal 'philosopher-king' monarchy he espoused in *The Republic*). Plato's island warranted little attention until 1627, when Sir Francis Bacon in *The New Atlantis* suggested that it was buried somewhere in the Americas, kicking off a frantic search that has led scientists and historians – sometimes reputable, often not – to place the lost civilisation as far afield as Cuba, the Azores, Cyprus and England.

If Atlantis did have a real geographical location, it was most likely on Crete, home of the Minoan civilisation. In 1500BC, when the Minoans dominated the Mediterranean as a naval and military power, a massive volcanic eruption blew apart the nearby island of Santorini. Hinted at in the Jason and the Argonauts myth (they experienced a pall of darkness, perhaps caused by the expulsion of volcanic ash into the atmosphere, and were pelted with fragments of rock by a fiery giant), the eruption reverberated throughout the ancient world. The tsunamis unleashed by this massive explosion, with waves up to 200m high, would have easily wiped out the Minoans, echoing the earthquakes and floods that finished off the fabled city of Atlantis.

Four other lost continents and mythical lands

1 The Southern Continent (*Terra Australis Incognita*)

The Greeks were the first to reason that there had to be a massive continent, equal in size to all of Asia and Europe, lying somewhere in the southern hemisphere. According to Aristotle, nature demanded symmetry, so the expansive lands they knew had to be matched on the other side of the globe. Ptolemy reasoned that this *terra incognita* (unknown land) stretched right up to India, and was warm, fertile and filled with riches, separated from the northern hemisphere by a hot belt of fire. Despite the fact that explorers were beginning to punch more and more holes in Ptolemy's theory, his fantastical ideas still loomed large in the European imagination until the 18th century – in the late 16th century, an unknown cartographer even mapped out this 'Antarctica', replete with beautiful forests and exotic animals. Australia and New Zealand were originally thought to be the northern tip of this great land; however, further exploration revealed the fabled Antarctica to be an icy, barren wilderness, less than one-tenth the size of the promised land of legend.

2 Frisland

In the mid-16th century, the Venetian geographer and writer Nicolò Zeno, bitter that the Genoese Christopher Columbus was getting all the credit for discovering America, set about constructing an elaborate hoax. He produced letters supposedly written by his great-great-great-grandfathers Antonio and Nicolò Zeno which related their discovery in the 14th century of a great island in the North Atlantic, Frisland, full of natural resources and savage natives. From here they sailed to the American coast more than a century before Columbus' voyage. Unbelievably, the hoax worked. Mercator included Frisland on his 1569 map of the world and the great English explorer Martin Frobisher thought he'd found it in the late 1570s (he'd actually 'found' Greenland, then owned by Norway). With a patriotic flourish, he proudly claimed the made-up island for England, and in 1577 Parliament officially declared Queen Elizabeth the master of Frisland and Estotiland (another Zeno invention), two of the first possessions of the nascent British empire. Unfortunately neither of them existed.

3 Lemuria

In the 19th century, before we knew of the supercontinent of Pangaea and continental drift, scientists investigating the new field of evolutionary biology were struggling with the question of how so many related primates had become scattered around the Indian and Pacific oceans. Lemurs in Madagascar were a particular problem: how did an animal descended from primates in India – which can't swim – make it to an African island? The zoologist Philip Sclater, a disciple of Darwin, came up with an ingenious solution: there must have been a great landmass parked between Africa and India that sank beneath the Indian Ocean after the last ice age tens of thousands of years ago. Christened Lemuria, his creation was swiftly picked up by scientists and writers across the globe. HG Wells suggested that it could have been the cradle of civilisation and the point from which humans colonised the planet.

4 Mu

Tied together in folklore and modern mysticism with the mythical Lemuria is the ancient land of Mu. While the Atlantic had its Atlantis and the Indian Ocean had Lemuria, in the mid-19th century the Pacific was notably free of mildly bonkers 'lost' continents. Madame Blavatsky, queen of the New Age Movement, had attempted to edge Lemuria out of the Indian and into the Pacific; however it took a slightly iffy reading of Mayan pictograms by a Catholic clergyman to finally confirm the idea that a huge island, Mu, lay beneath the Pacific waves. Charles-Etienne Brasseur de Bourbourg, a 19th-century French abbé, was convinced of the ancient links between Amerindian and East Asian culture, and using a Mayan 'alphabet' invented by a conquistador monk (the Mayan writing system wasn't letter based, making such an alphabet impossible), he discovered references to a continent used as a land-bridge over the Pacific that had been buried under the water after a cataclysmic volcanic eruption. By the mid-Twenties Mu was being used to explain the origin of the Pacific Islands, and – as often seems to happen to these lost worlds – it was posited as the birthplace of humanity. The general acceptance of the science of continental-drift theory in the mid-20th century finally killed off the wild Mu myth.

Muhammed al-Idrisi

(b. 1099; d. 1165)
Moroccan cartographer

Muhammed al-Idrisi was one of the finest
mapmakers of the Middle Ages, creating maps
that were remarkably accurate for the time
(pictured). Born in Sabtah (modern-day Ceuta), Morocco, al-Idrisi
spent much of his youth travelling. Passing through Muslim Spain
and breaking into Christian France and Britain, he even made it to
Asia Minor by the age of 16, scribbling notes as he went. In 1138, after
studying in Cordoba, al-Idrisi was invited to the court of Roger II of
Sicily, a Norman ruler whose father, Roger I, had seized the island
from the Arabs only a few decades earlier.

Roger II had invited al-Idrisi to his court for one purpose: to create
a map of the world so detailed it could work as a summary of all the
knowledge the Greek and Arab geographers had accumulated over
the past 1,000 years. Christian maps of the age were largely symbolic
and fanciful, full of dragons to the east and the Garden of Eden in the
north, while Arab mariners' charts, though detailed, were confined to
only the most popular waterways. It took 15 years for al-Idrisi and his
team to sift through books, scrolls and interview thousands of sailors, before they could finally set to work carving the map onto a great
silver disc, or planisphere, weighing 150kg and measuring more than
2m in diameter. It is now, sadly, lost – but we know through copies
that its superiority over contemporary maps was striking.

However, his accompanying geographical guidebook, the *Al-Kitab
al-Rujari* or *Roger's Book*, is arguably an even greater achievement.
Writing about the climate, peoples and resources of each of the great
regions and continents, al-Idrisi gave detailed descriptions of such
places as Russia, Ghana and Britain. During an uprising of Sicilian
barons in 1160, in which many documents were destroyed, al-Idrisi
escaped to North Africa. *Roger's Book* was published in Arabic in Rome
in 1592, but it was not until the 17th century that his groundbreaking
work was published in Latin and became accessible to Europeans.

Romancing the stone

The origin of birthstones

Until the beginning of the 20th century, birthstones – stones which some believe reflect each month of the year and hold powerful potential – varied over time and changed according to country and belief system. One of the first references to birthstones comes from the Bible. Revelation 21:19-20 lists 12 stones which correspond to the months of the Roman calendar. They are: jasper, sapphire, chalcedony, emerald, sardonyx, sardius, chrysolyte, beryl, topaz, chrysoprasus, jacinth and amethyst. However, in 1912 the Jewelers of America standardised the birthstones and today we generally recognise these stones...

January Garnet Associated with faith, eternity and truth, garnet – a silicate mineral – is also supposed to prevent accidents during travel.

February Amethyst Most attractive are the rich, deep-purple amethysts – a significant colour for the Romans, who saw it as a sign of nobility. The semi-precious stone was also a firm favourite of the Victorians, who used it in much of their jewellery. The stone's name comes from the ancient Greek word *amethystos*, meaning 'not drunk' – and it was once believed that if these stones were added to your glass of wine you'd remain sober.

March Aquamarine One of the most common forms of beryl gems (emeralds are of the same family), aquamarine is named for its seawater-like colour (from the Latin words *aqua*, meaning 'water' and *marina*, meaning 'of the sea') and is believed to bring happiness and understanding.

April Diamond The hardest of all gemstones, diamond takes its name from the Greek word *adamas* meaning 'unconquerable'. Now marketed as the perfect stone for engagement rings, diamonds were said to have formed the tips of Cupid's arrows.

May Emerald Cut from the Cleopatra Mines near the Red Sea in Egypt as early as 2000BC, emeralds (possibly from the Sanskrit word for green) have held a special significance for many people around the world, with their deep-green colour symbolising springtime, life and fertility. Today many of the world's fine emeralds come from Brazil and Colombia and are associated with fidelity, goodness and love as well as the 55th wedding anniversary.

June Moonstone It was believed you could see the waxing and waning moon in the shimmer of this pale blue stone. In India, wearing one at night is thought to bring on beautiful dreams.

July Ruby The most highly prized blood-red rubies come from Burma, where they have been dug from the Mogok region for thousands of years. Rubies from over the border in Thailand display a brown tinge, while Sri Lankan rubies have a more pink hue. Often set alongside diamonds in engagement rings, rubies embody love, enthusiasm and strength, and mark the 40th wedding anniversary.

August Peridot A green stone – often yellowish, pistaccio or bottle green – peridot was originally referred to as topaz, although it is in fact a different type of gem. It is linked with success, peace and luck, and its name – from the Greek *peridona* – means 'plentiful'.

September Sapphire Although it is most often considered a blue gem, sapphire can be found in pinks, greens and purples and is a member of the corundums (a crystalline form of aluminium oxide). All corundum gems of any colour other than red are sapphires; red corundums are rubies. Black sapphires are found in Australia and cornflower blue ones in Sri Lanka.

October Opal, Rose zircon Softer, iridescent gems formed in layers, opals were most famously found along Lightning Ridge in Australia, where black opals with flashes of colour were highly prized – in fact the word opal derives from the Greek *opallos*, meaning 'to see a change of colour'. Today these mines have been all but cleared out.

November Topaz The stone of wisdom and courage can be found in the Cairngorms in Scotland and the Mountains of Mourne in Northern Ireland, and has been used in Celtic jewellery. It comes in shades of brown and rich sherry, although it is more common in white and blue. Heat-treating yellow topaz can produce pink gems.

December Turquoise, Blue topaz This opaque green-blue stone was mined in Persia, and many of the pieces of jewellery discovered in Egyptian tombs were encrusted with it. It is found in thin seams among sandstone and limonite rocks and is associated with happiness.

Gordon Wright

Dowsers tend to use either 'L' rods or 'V' and 'Y' rods. Traditionally these rods were wooden twigs shaped like these letters, but I now use plastic V-shaped rods. You can feel the difference between a plastic and wooden rod – whenever I use wood I tend to get through two or three rods per site, as they seem to keep a memory of what I've located with them in the past. If I find water with a wooden rod, I could go 100 miles away and still get the same readings; plastic rods don't do that. Whether this is the instruments or just me I don't know – it's just what happens. The instruments work as an indicator, interpreting what the body feels, but there are people who can dowse without any instruments at all.

If I'm looking for a bore hole, I'll use two rods, one heavier than the other. I'll begin by standing in a field holding the heavier one high up in front of me. Gradually it will pull down to wherever the attraction is. If I then use it like a rifle sight, it will point me to roughly where I need to go from up to half a mile away. Once I've walked over to where this rod has located a fault, I'll switch to a lighter rod to pinpoint exactly where the faults are. Once this is done, I'll use the rods to measure the depth of the bore hole. To do this I straddle the fault zone, holding the rod vertically. Then I let it rotate – every complete rotation of the rod is equal to 10ft underground – and when it stops, indicating that there is a change (for instance from black clay to brown clay, or a crack in the rocks), it will swing, giving an idea as to how wide the change in polarity is.

From that point on it is down to guesswork as to what the change may be. You have to ascertain whether it's between two types of clay or because the ground is fractured – neither of which will provide water – or because there's a fault with a solid base, which will support water. It's all about the feeling you get – you just know what type of fault there is, and whether there's water down there or not.

Sometimes I can even differentiate between dirty and clean water – dirty water just doesn't feel right – but I've found the water in this country is so full of contaminants that have leaked through the soil that it can be very hard. You get to notice slight changes in the rod with experience. With hard rock formations I can get the depth to within inches, but most of the time we're looking at a 4ft to 5ft margin of error. With clays I've been out by 20ft. This does seem to be typical with all dowsers: clay is always difficult. We have no idea why.

You can locate everything from oil to gold to lost golf balls through dowsing, but I tend to focus on finding water. I leave looking for things like pipelines or metals to others. I do quite a bit of work for other drilling companies – when they get stuck they call me in – but the majority of my work is for private landowners, mostly smallholders and farmers looking for a usable supply of water on their property.

I'm successful around 94% to 95% of the time, but I have a 5% to 6% failure rate, which comes from misreadings. One of the problems is that if you pre-empt what you're looking for – if you expect to find water in a certain place – you'll pick up a reading of water when it might not be there. You've got to be completely open-minded. People have come up with all sorts of theories: when we use metal, people say it's all to do with the magnetic field, but many use wood quite effectively. The only way I can describe it is that at some point something happened underground to change the 'polation' at certain points, and when these events occurred energy was released, and some of this energy is stored underground. Water moving underground creates energy. I believe it's this energy that we pick up in muscular twitches which lead us to the source. A lot of people claim dowsing is a spiritual thing, but I disagree. It's just one of those phenomena for which there's no valid explanation. I mean, you walk into a field with a bit of plastic and say: 'If you dig a hole here to 100m, you're going to get usable water.' It sounds like a load of bull, but it does work. **GORDON WRIGHT**

Gordon Wright has been a water diviner for more than 35 years in Southern Africa and the UK and runs the Wright Drilling Company, which is based in the West Midlands. He estimates that around 80% of people are capable of dowsing

On shifting ground

An introduction to plate tectonics

The acceptance of the plate tectonic theory was one of the great scientific turnabouts of the 20th century, providing a unifying and fundamental theory of the formation and development of the Earth's surface.

As far back as the 16th century, cartographers had noticed that the west coast of Africa was a close fit with the east coast of Latin America, but no theory could explain why.

In 1912, the German scientist Alfred Wegener proposed the controversial idea of continental drift to explain the phenomenon. He noticed the similarity between fossils and rocks on continents separated by oceans, and the jigsaw puzzle-like nature of the continents themselves. This led him to believe that they had once formed a single supercontinent, which he dubbed Pangaea (Greek for 'All Lands'), and subsequently drifted apart. Wegener's theory was widely ridiculed at the time.

However, improvements in dating the fossil and rock record began to support Wegener, and the discovery of marine fossils atop the world's great mountain chains fitted with his idea of uplift caused by colliding land masses. In the Fifties, the superpowers' atomic submarines began monitoring and mapping the ocean floor to a greater degree than ever before. They observed hitherto unknown geological features such as ocean-floor ridges and trenches, and seismic activity at these locations. In 1962 the American geologist Harry Hess updated Wegener's ideas, concluding that the ocean floor and its adjoining continent moved together on the same crustal plate.

How the theory works

The Earth's surface is made up of seven major, and several minor, tectonic plates of light density granite (known collectively as the lithosphere) floating on a 'sea' of high-density basalt (known as the asthenosphere). These plates are ever moving at varying rates, from a few millimetres to 2cm a year (the speed at which our nails grow) to 16cm a year (the speed at which our hair grows). The meeting points of the plates are known as faults, and the tremendous energy and friction which are built up can lead to traumatic geological events such as earthquakes and volcanic eruptions, and the creation of mountains and ocean trenches. There are three types of plate boundary...

Divergent When two plates diverge, land valleys such as Kenya's Rift Valley and ocean ridges such as the Mid-Atlantic Ridge are often formed. Ocean ridges are created as magma, or molten rock, wells up to fill the gap created by the spreading plates.

Convergent When plates converge, the less dense (often oceanic) plate tends to slide under the denser (continental) one in a process known as subduction. This movement creates ocean trenches and mountain ranges. Over the past 50 million years, the Himalayas were formed in this way as the Indo-Australian plate collided with the Eurasian plate at a rate of around 67mm per year, forcing the mountain range to rise by 5mm per year.

Transform Where two plates slide past each other, the friction caused can trigger earthquakes. The San Andreas fault, where the Pacific and North American plates meet, has been the site of many such events, including the massive San Francisco earthquake of 1906 and numerous subsequent destructive tremors. Fear of this phenomenon led to Superman (in the original movie) and James Bond in *View to a Kill* preventing villains from exploding large bombs along the fault – though such explosions would be of no consequence due to the vastness of the forces involved. TOM TEMPLETON

The Earth's continents by size

1 Asia	44,579,000 sq km
2 Africa	30,065,000 sq km
3 North America	24,256,000 sq km
4 South America	17,819,000 sq km
5 Antarctica	13,209,000 sq km
6 Europe	9,938,000 sq km
7 Australia/Oceania	7,687,000 sq km

Uniting the world

The supercontinent cycle

In his book *Supercontinent*, Ted Nield of the British Geological Society describes the great ebb and flow of the continents as 'the grandest of all the patterns in nature'. The 'pulse' of Mother Earth, the supercontinent cycle, as it's known, has acted as a catalyst for the flourishing of life and its subsequent apocalyptic extinctions, the planet's bleak ice ages and blistering summers. The theory explains how the vagaries of plate tectonics cause the massive continental landmasses, or cratons, to wander the surface of the Earth, joining together into immense supercontinents, only to break apart again hundreds of millions of years later in cycles lasting up to 500 million years.

At least one supercontinent exists today: Eurasia, formed when the European, Asian, Indian and Arabian landmasses were welded together around 50m years ago. The Americas (joined by the Isthmus of Panama), as well as Afro-Eurasia (referencing the joining of the continents of Africa and Eurasia at the Isthmus of Suez) have both been suggested as other possible modern supercontinents. The great supercontinents of the past are the fruits of nearly a century of intense investigation. Using a combination of paleomagnetism (the study of fossil magnetism in rocks to find out where rocks formed) and geochronology (studying radioactive decay to discover when rocks formed), we can hazard reasonable guesses as to the countries and continents that may have been bonded together in the distant past. The most obvious clue picked up by the first geologists to suggest supercontinents, however, came from simply looking at a world map. The continents resemble giant jigsaw pieces, with the jutting shape of Brazil seeming to fit perfectly into the Gulf of Guinea in West Africa.

These supercontinents eventually break apart, as they block the flow of heat from the Earth's interior, causing the crust to bulge upward and crack, with magma rushing through the gap and forcing the new continental fragments apart. Why continental drift causes them to then rejoin is still unknown: current theories include the dissipation of heat from the Earth's mantle, the relative densities of the lithosphere and the asthenosphere, and the drag of the Moon. Our knowledge is limited to just a few of these great ancient landmasses – but many more great supercontinents may well have been lost in the mists of time.

The last three supercontinents

Rodinia (c1,100-750 million years ago) The true Eden. It was around Rodinia's shores that complex life first evolved – indeed, its name comes from the Russian *rodina*, meaning motherland. The supercontinent, comprising almost every craton (or protocontinent, such as India and Siberia), straddled the equator, leaving the poles land-free. Rodinia existed in one of the most revolutionary periods of the Earth's history, as oxygen levels in the atmosphere shot up and the planet entered a period of unrivalled stability. The Cryogenian period (850-630m years ago) saw this stability, and Rodinia itself, disappear as the Earth froze over in one of the planet's most severe ice ages.

Gondwana (650-130m years ago) During the 100m years following Rodinia's break-up, the units of Australia-Antarctica and South America-Africa moved towards the South Pole. These vast landmasses moved together, along with the smaller India, South East Asia, Florida and Arabia cratons, to form the great southern super-continent Gondwana. It was here that a huge variety of flora and fauna flourished – organic matter which formed vast coal reserves.

Pangaea (350-180m years ago) While Gondwana was forming around the South Pole, the other remnants of Rodinia – Laurentia (most of North America and Greenland), Baltica (Europe), Avalonia (the UK and Nova Scotia) and Siberia – drifted together around the equator, forming the Appalachian Mountains. At this time the Sahara sat at the South Pole, while Siberia was equatorial and lush. Some 350m years ago Gondwana and this new landmass joined together to form the mighty Pangaea, which was home to the dinosaurs in its arid early days, and the site of the first major diversification of mammals just as it was beginning to break apart. After Pangaea disintegrated, the continents – freed from the largest of all supercontinents – slowly drifted around the globe to their current positions.

Ten films about the Earth

Planet of the Apes (1968, **Franklin J Schaffner**) In the distant future, a spaceship crashes onto a planet strangely similar to Earth which is ruled by talking apes and where man is the enslaved animal.

Earthquake (1974, **Mark Robson**) Charlton Heston fails to stop a massive earthquake from destroying Los Angeles.

Blue Planet (1990, **Ben Burtt**) A visually awesome study of the Earth, with views from space, land and under water, showing all the systems that ensure our planet's survival.

Baraka (1992, **Ron Fricke**) A wordless visual poem moving casually from epic volcanos and lush forests to logging and strip mining, and the slow destruction of the Earth's beauty by man.

Volcano (1997, **Mick Jackson**) Puzzlingly, a volcano appears in central Los Angeles over the course of a week. Tommy Lee Jones, with his plucky seismologist sidekick Anne Heche, saves the day.

Dante's Peak (1997, **Roger Donaldson**) Pierce Brosnan fails to convince the city council that the nearby dormant volcano will erupt – until it does just that.

Ice Age (2002, **Chris Wedge and Carlos Saldanha**) Some 20,000 years ago, when the Earth is primarily a frozen wasteland, a sabre-toothed tiger, a mammoth, a sloth and a human toddler embark on a quest – and cartoon fun ensues.

Touching the Void (2003, **Kevin Macdonald**) Two climbers attempt to scale the Siula Grande in the Peruvian Andes but come unstuck on the descent when one breaks a leg. In the battle of man versus mountain, both climbers somehow survive. Based on a true story.

The Core (2003, **Jon Amiel**) The Earth's core stops rotating for no apparent reason and a group of scientists must drill down and solve the problem with the help of a nuclear bomb.

An Inconvenient Truth (2006, **Davis Guggenheim**) Genuinely powerful Al Gore lecture on global warming which focuses on a simple message: the Earth is heading for disaster unless we kick our carbon addiction.

The Tropic lines

TROPICO DE CANCER

The imaginary Tropic lines searing their way above and below the equator on any modern map mark the point at which the Sun is directly overhead at noon on the two annual solstices (the word solstice itself comes from the Latin *sol* mean-ing 'Sun' and *sistere* meaning 'to stand still'). On the June solstice, the Sun is directly overhead at every point along the Tropic of Cancer and during the December solstice it is overhead along the Tropic of Capricorn, marking the very height of summer for the northern and southern hemispheres, respectively. The tropics (the region between the two lines) is an area without seasons, as the Sun is always high in the sky.

The Tropic lines take their names from the fact that when the ancients first identified them some 2,000 years ago, the Sun was entering the constellation of Cancer during the summer and Capri-corn in the winter. Due to a complex series of astronomical factors which gradually shift the Earth in relation to the constellations, the two Tropics are now technically located in Taurus and Sagittarius – although the amount we'd have to spend altering maps would prob-ably bankrupt a thousand geography departments.

The 'wobble' of the Earth also means that the Tropic lines are in fact moving, as the axial tilt (the angle at which the Earth tilts away from its orbital plane) gradually shifts. As this angle varies, so must the positions of the Tropic lines, making the tropics expand and contract over 41,000-year-long cycles. Currently the two lines are drift-ing towards the equator at a rate of 15m per year, meaning that the trop-ics are shrinking by 1,100 sq km annually.

LINEA DEL TROPICO DE CAPRICORNIO

Going underground

The Hollow Earth theory

When Plato wrote of 'enormous subterranean tunnels both broad and narrow' under the Earth's surface, he could hardly have imagined that the idea would become an obsession for many searching for an earthly paradise.

In 1692 the English astronomer Edmond Halley (of comet fame) proposed one of the first Hollow Earth theories. The Earth, he declared, is not hollow but is actually composed of four habitable concentric spheres stacked like Russian dolls. Each sphere, he reasoned, is illuminated by a luminous atmosphere and each has its own independent magnetic poles. Killing two scientific birds with one stone, he then went on to suggest that the Aurora Borealis is in fact gas escaping through the Earth's thin crust from these luminous atmospheres which lie below. Thus not only was a theory born, but a quest practically demanded: find the source of the escaping gas and you've found the entrance to these subterranean worlds.

Of course, variations on the theme followed. Swiss mathematician Leonhard Euler led the brainstorming, replacing the multiple-spheres theory with a single hollow sphere containing a sun 600 miles wide. Scottish physicist and mathematician Sir John Leslie went on to assert that there were actually two suns, Pluto and Proserpine.

But who would actually venture forth to find this secret land? In 1818, American ex-army officer and businessman John Cleves Symmes – who believed that there were giant apertures at both the North and South Poles leading to the interior – published an article in which he solemnly declared his intent: 'To all the World: I declare the Earth is hollow and habitable within; containing a number of solid concentric spheres, one within the other, and that it is open at the poles 12 or 16 degrees.' Symmes devoted his life to advancing his theory, and tried unsuccessfully to raise funds for a polar expedition intended to prove the existence of this 1,400 mile-wide entrance to the inner Earth – named Symmes' Hole in his honour.

At the end of the 19th century, Cyrus Reed Teed, an American doctor, proposed a truly radical reworking of the Hollow Earth theory in what he termed 'cellular cosmogony'. Instead of believing in a globe in which there are other hidden worlds, he flipped the idea and suggested that in fact we live on the inside of a giant sphere. At its centre lies our Sun, half light and half dark, giving the appearance of sunrise and sunset. Conveniently, the atmosphere is too dense to be able to see across to the other side of the world. Remarkably, Teed found fellow believers and started a cult based on his idea called Koreshanity. Unsurprisingly, he died never having proved his theory correct.

The notion of the Hollow Earth did not die with Teed. It has been suggested that the Nazis investigated his theories – sending an expedition to the island of Rungen in the Baltic to spy on the British fleet by looking skyward. And in 1969, Symmes' theory was brought up to date by Dr Raymond Bernard – the pseudonym of Dr Walter Siegmeister – in his book *The Hollow Earth*. There were holes at the poles, he said, but rather than a pre-lapsarian paradise lying within there lives an advanced civilisation complete with flying saucers. Of course proof was thin on the ground.

Five novels about the Hollow Earth

Nicolai Klimii iter Subterraneum by **Ludvig Holberg (1741)** Nicolai Klim discovers a world inhabited by 'trees with human heads and little feet on which they creep about' within the Earth.

Icosaméron by **Jacques Casanova (1788)** This 1,800-page epic tells of a brother and sister who fall into a land of brightly coloured dwarfs.

The Narrative of Arthur Gordon Pym of Nantucket by **Edgar Allan Poe (1838)** What begins as a seafaring adventure rapidly becomes more complex with ideas gleaned from Symmes' Hollow Earth.

A Journey to the Centre of the Earth by **Jules Verne (1864)** A professor, his nephew and their guide enter a volcano in Iceland.

Dorothy and the Wizard in Oz by **L Frank Baum (1908)** The fourth in Baum's famous Oz series, this book sees an earthquake open a crevice through which Dorothy falls, arriving in the land of the Mangaboos.

Stanley Williams

We need more eruptions. If we have more eruptions, people will be more regularly reminded that volcanos are incredibly hazardous. Five hundred million people around the world are living within reach of an eruption. In the city of Quito, Ecuador, 2m people are living on the slopes of Pichincha volcano. If Vesuvius were to blow today, it's estimated that 100,000 people could perish. The national symbol of Japan, Mount Fuji, is a volcano and sitting next door to Tokyo. An eruption is a blink-of-an-eye sort of thing – all of a sudden the door opens and it's death.

Volcanologists go to volcanos when they're heating up because that's when we can learn the most about forecasting eruptions, which is basically the prize. Galeras in Colombia was, and still is, fascinating, dangerous and active and accessible – making it a good laboratory. I was on Galeras with a group of scientists in 1993. I remember the climb up there, chatting with Igor Menyailov and Geoff Brown and the others, and we were all so happy to be there, working together in the crater, and the spirit was so good. Igor was taking readings from the gases bubbling out of the fumaroles, Geoff was taking the volcano's pulse with a gravimeter – 100m times more sensitive than a grocer's scale. We were trying to work out if the magma was on the move. Suddenly boulders began cascading down, and then the air was rent by a thunderclap and then the sound of the Earth's crust snapping. Nine people were killed, including five of my colleagues. It's still hard to take it in.

I went back a year later but I didn't go into the crater – I'd just had the wire birdcage removed from my shattered legs, so I wasn't strong enough. But in August 1995 I was back and working. Almost every forward step in volcanology has followed in the footsteps of disaster. Galeras has continued to be a spectacular source of knowledge and a testing ground for new instruments.

The discipline has been going since at least 79AD. Pliny the Younger wrote an incredibly detailed report of the eruption of Vesuvius – his observations are still cornerstones of the science. Field data has been collected throughout history, sometimes inadvertently. People used to think that Edvard Munch was crazy because of the mad red and yellow sky in his painting *The Scream*. But he painted it a few days after Krakatoa erupted in Indonesia in 1883, and some models of the atmosphere have shown that Oslo harbour would have had those sorts of horrible skies at that time. Krakatoa's blast was heard 2,900 miles away and 36,000 people died, mostly from huge tsunamis whipped up by the blast.

However probably the biggest eruption of the last 10,000 years took place at Tambora, Indonesia in 1815. Tambora killed 12,000, mainly from pyroclastic flows – speeding clouds of gas and ash. Temperatures dropped around the world as a result of the aerosols and dust in the stratosphere. Turner painted the distinctive red sunsets over New England that resulted.

We've made great strides in our ability to forecast. The eruption of Pinatubo in the Philippines back in 1993 was a great success story. The volcano was gearing up and then it went quiet. The seismology team said it was becoming more and more constipated and could release a huge amount of energy. As a result of the team's advice, thousands of soldiers were evacuated from the nearby air force base, and thousands of villagers. By the time it spectacularly erupted, many, many lives had been saved.

But scientists are often not listened to – what we call the 'International Chamber of Commerce' doesn't want us stopping the wheels of business turning. In 1985 at Ruiz, Colombia, the scientists who encouraged evacuation were called 'volcano terrorists'. Three days later their prediction of where the people were most at risk was proved tragically accurate, as 23,000 people were killed by mudflows.

One of the things we're up against is that people don't like being reminded that we are little gnats running around this sphere. If you look back at the big eruptions of the world, they happened with a frequency that is not negligible. If we were to have an eruption that killed a million people, it wouldn't be a surprise. **STANLEY WILLIAMS**

Stanley Williams is professor of geology at Arizona State University

A volcano

The Romans believed that the tiny Mediterranean island of Vulcano was the chimney of the forge of Vulcan, the blacksmith of the gods, who would emit fragments of cloud and dust as he hammered out bolts of lightning for Jupiter. In the 2,000 years since, our knowledge of volcanos, to which the tiny island gave its name, has exploded.

Formed in a similar way to mountains, by the pushing together or pulling apart of the planet's vast tectonic plates, volcanos slowly grow over vents in the Earth's surface connected to reservoirs of molten rock that form in the mantle. As pressure builds up beneath the surface, molten rock is forced past the less dense solid rock surrounding it until it eventually breaks through weaknesses in the crust, allowing lava and ash to flood out. A common result is a pyroclastic flow – fast-moving currents of hot gas and rock (known collectively as tephra) with temperatures of up to 1,000C which rush down the slopes of a volcano at speeds of more than 50mph, destroying everything in their path.

There are several different types of volcano. A stratovolcano forms as successive large eruptions leave layers of ash and rock behind, the volcano growing with every explosive discharge. Lava domes can form during slow eruptions, which cause the lava to solidify in rocky bubbles. Meanwhile, monstrous supervolcanos form calderas, massive craters, rather than mountains. It is thought that the Lake Toba supervolcano eruption in Indonesia 75,000 years ago caused a worldwide 'volcanic winter' that reduced the human population to just a few thousand. The supervolcano in Yellowstone National Park, Wyoming is still considered to be active.

Most volcanos today are found in and around the 40,000km Ring of Fire, a chain of volcanos which trace the Pacific coasts of North and South America, Japan, Indonesia and New Zealand, where the sheer amount of tectonic activity has caused the Earth's surface to weaken, allowing magma to push through.

It's a blast

The Volcanic Explosivity Index (VEI)

The Volcanic Explosivity Index (VEI) was drawn up in 1982 to describe the relative size or magnitude of explosive volcanic eruptions. The VEI assigns a number to each volcanic explosion based on the volume of erupted pyroclastic material (ashfall and pyroclastic flows for example), the height of the eruption column and the eruption's duration. The magnitude of a volcanic explosion is then measured on a scale from 0-to-8, along which each increase in value represents a jump by a factor of 10 – which means that the explosions in Long Valley and Yellowstone almost 1 million years ago were 1,000 times more powerful than the eruption of Mount St Helens in 1980.

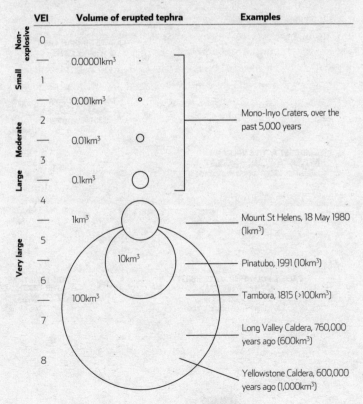

VEI	Volume of erupted tephra	Examples
Non-explosive 0		
Small 1	0.00001km³	
	0.001km³	
Moderate 2	0.01km³	Mono-Inyo Craters, over the past 5,000 years
3		
Large 4	0.1km³	
	1km³	Mount St Helens, 18 May 1980 (1km³)
Very large 5	10km³	Pinatubo, 1991 (10km³)
6	100km³	Tambora, 1815 (>100km³)
7		Long Valley Caldera, 760,000 years ago (600km³)
8		Yellowstone Caldera, 600,000 years ago (1,000km³)

Our superlative planet

Earth's highest, deepest, longest and largest...

LARGEST ISLAND
GREENLAND
823,000 sq miles

.... **LARGEST URBAN AREA**
NEW YORK
4,349 sq miles

LARGEST DESERT
SAHARA ....
3,320,000 sq miles

BIGGEST ACTIVE VOLCANO
MAUNA LOA, HAWAII
4,170m high, 19,000 cubic miles volume

.... **PACIFIC POLE OF INACCESSIBILITY**
POINT NEMO
28,52.6S; 123,23.6W
1,670 miles from nearest land

**POINT FURTHEST FROM
THE EARTH'S CORE**
MT CHIMBORAZO
3,967 miles

LARGEST COUNTRY
RUSSIA
6,591027 sq miles

LARGEST LAKE
CASPIAN SEA
143,244 sq miles

**LOWEST POINT
ON DRY LAND**
DEAD SEA
418m below sea level

EURASIAN POLE OF INACCESSIBILITY
URUQI, XINJIANG, CHINA
1,645 miles from nearest coastline

LARGEST SEA
**SOUTH CHINA
SEA**
1,351,000 sq miles

LARGEST RIVER
NILE
4,160 miles

DEEPEST POINT
**CHALLENGER DEEP,
MARIANA TRENCH**
6.77-6.84 miles deep

HIGHEST MOUNTAIN
MT EVEREST
8,848 metres

LARGEST OCEAN
PACIFIC
69,375,000 sq miles

Gerardus Mercator

(b. 5 March 1512; d. 2 December 1594)
Flemish cartographer

A Renaissance mapmaker of international renown, Gerardus Mercator took cartography into the modern era, creating several impressive globes and world maps, as well as coining the word atlas to describe a collection of maps. His most famous achievement was the invention of the Mercator projection, which conquered the problem of fitting the spherical world onto a rectangular map by distorting it slightly – something which today may seem straightforward, but in the mid-16th century, when the age of exploration was at its peak, was revolutionary.

Born Gheert Cremer in Rupelmonde, in modern-day Belgium, Mercator (meaning merchant) initially had a passion for philosophy. His Protestant beliefs eventually turned him against the discipline, and he delved into geography as a way of exploring God's creation. He began studying at the University of Leuven under the great mathematician and cartographer Gemma Frisius, with whom he created his first globe. Mercator made a detailed biblical map of Palestine in 1537, his first solo project, which he followed up in 1538 with the first world map to show the Americas as two distinct entities, which he named northern and southern America. In 1564 he was appointed court cosmographer to Wilhelm, Duke of Jülich-Cleves-Berg.

Mercator drew his first world map using his eponymous projection in 1569 – to the world's mariners it was a godsend. Although the projection heavily distorted the size of certain countries – Greenland became the same size as Africa and Alaska equal to Brazil – now sailors could plot their courses simply by placing a compass on the map and sailing in that direction. Today, Mercator maps are still used by sailors, but they have largely been removed from classrooms after a campaign by mapmaking rivals denouncing the projection as 'racist' because it shrank Africa and other developing countries in comparison with the exaggerated size of Europe, the US and Australia.

Mapmaking

The story of the Ordnance Survey

Today the Ordnance Survey is the world's leading mapmaker, having lovingly detailed all of Britain's 440 million geographical features, including 321,000 miles of road (enough to encircle the equator 13 times), all 11,072 miles of coastline and around 26m letterboxes.

It all started back in 1791, when the French – in the throes of revolution – looked set to attempt a daring attack across the channel. The government ordered its defence ministry – then called the Board of Ordnance – to create a detailed map, or survey, of the vulnerable south coast. The first Ordnance Survey map, a 1:63,360 (one inch to the mile) representation of Kent, was released in 1801 (ironically just as the French threat was quelled at the battle of Trafalgar), and within 20 years a third of England and Wales had been mapped to a previously unimaginable level of detail.

> **"** *A road map always tells you everything except how to refold it.*
>
> Anonymous

Creating the maps was a slow, laborious task. Thomas Colby, the Survey's director general, walked 586 miles in just 22 days on one reconnaissance trek in 1819. In 1840 builders of the new railway network required more and more detailed maps, so the government expanded the institution and ordered it to map all of Britain, bestowing upon the surveyors the legal right to 'enter into and upon any land' in the process. During the First World War, OS surveyors joined the troops in Europe, creating maps of Belgium, France and the Netherlands to help the war effort, while the Allied armies in the Second World War devoured the Ordnance Survey's creations – 120m maps were used during the Normandy landings alone.

These days the OS has become a thoroughly modern institution. In 1995 Britain became the first country in the world to be digitally mapped, and the new OS MasterMap is one of the most reliable in the world, with more than 5,000 updates added daily and 1m changes to the UK landscape recorded every year.

Shape shifting

Five maps charting our changing world

Our understanding of the planet's landscape and geography has slowly coalesced over the last 2,000 years like the vast tectonic plates which make up the Earth's crust. This selection of maps demonstrates how we've slowly built up a picture of our globe in all its majesty as 'a sparkling blue and white jewel' suspended in space, as US moon-walker Edgar Mitchell memorably put it.

1 Early Christian 'T-O' Map (7th century AD)

Christian maps of the Middle Ages regressed from the detailed charts of the Greeks and Romans, settling on this rather spare diagram. The 'O' represents the known universe, with Jerusalem at its centre, and the 'T' represents its main waterways. It is orientated with east at the top, beyond which, it was believed, lay paradise.

2 Muhammed al-Idrisi's *Tabula Rogeriana* (1154)

Part of the *Al-Kitab al-Rujari* (*Roger's Book*), al-Idrisi's world map was one of the most detailed of its time, and was used by sailors and explorers for centuries after its creation.

3 Martin Waldseemüller's *Universalis Cosmographia* (1507)

One of the first maps to show the New World in all its strange glory, Waldseemüller's map also includes the first known reference to the name America.

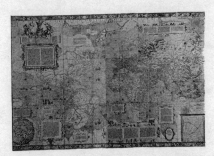

4 Gerardus Mercator's *Nova et Aucta Orbis Terrae* (1569)

The first world map produced by the cartographer using his Mercator projection (note how Canada appears bigger than the whole of Africa). It was a brilliant innovation, which sailors used, but has now largely gone out of fashion.

5 Satellite image of the Earth

The first images of the Earth from space radically changed our perception of the planet. For the first time in history, we were truly able to look back at ourselves hanging in the infinite blackness of space.

Bob Gatliff

The oceans are a tremendously important part of our climate system, storing vast amounts of heat and playing an important role in recycling elements such as carbon. The shape of the seabed has a great affect on the ocean's circulation. For example, in the North Atlantic there's a huge oceanic ridge running from Greenland to northern Britain, and over the course of the Atlantic's history the height of this ridge has fluctuated. This has varied the amount of water circling in the oceans, inexorably changing climate and land formation. We can use marine geology to work out how this circulation has changed in the past, so we know for example that the last major event to happen was the closing of the ocean circulation between North and South America (with the joining at the Isthmus of Panama), which may have helped induce the previous ice age. So the geology of the oceans is a crucial part of understanding our climate, and how any changes in it occur.

> 66 *How inappropriate to call this planet Earth when it is quite clearly Ocean.*
>
> Arthur C Clarke

One of the key things we're doing at the moment is taking core samples through sediment from the last 2 million years and looking at them to see the records they hold of past periods of climate change. We can then use those records to predict how change may occur again in the future. When we came out of the last but one glaciation, about 250,000 years ago, it looks like world temperatures were about 3° warmer than they are now, so studying the sediments from that period provide a good model of what is likely to happen over the next 100 years as present temperatures climb. Contemporary evidence suggests that the Thermal Maximum, a period of intense global warming between the Paleocene and Eocene epochs, may have been caused by a massive release of methane. How this happened is unknown, but one major theory is that methane hydrates (a solid form of methane) stored under the cold ocean floor slowly released methane gas as the waters warmed up, which, if correct, could have profound consequences for us today, as it looks like massive amounts of methane hydrate are now stored under the slowly melting permafrost of Siberia.

About half of the carbon dioxide we've produced has gone straight into the oceans, which has made it more acidic (the pH of the oceans has declined by 0.1 since the Industrial Revolution – a huge decrease considering their vast size). This has already had an impact on shellfish populations, and it could well be that the acidity of the oceans will have a bigger impact on many species than climate change. At the moment this research is still in its early stages, but we should soon start receiving crucial information as to the mechanics of climate change.

British marine geologists have also been looking at the North Atlantic Ridge as a potential source of minerals in the future. Mining the ocean floor, as long as it's economically and technologically viable, is a very real possibility. However, for me the most interesting thing about the ridge is that it's very hot, and so there's a chance we could utilise that heat as an energy source, perhaps turning it into electricity and transmitting it back to Europe. That's a long-term venture, but as a source of renewable thermal energy it could be a fascinating avenue for research. The next big stage of offshore work, however, will be pumping CO_2 back out of the ocean and storing it under the North Sea, possibly in old oil and gas fields where it wouldn't cause harm.

At the moment there's a big debate up in Edinburgh about what to do about the Firth of Forth Bridge, which needs replacing. Do you build another bridge, a tunnel or a barrage with a road on top? With a barrage we could harness the river for tidal energy and stop future storms and floods, but marine biologists and geologists, myself included, will complain about the damage it would cause to the local environment. Yet the fact is that very soon we will have to start thinking less about these matters and more about protecting Edinburgh itself from rising sea levels and the growing risk of flooding, as well as the opportunity for renewable energy. Things will have to change. **BOB GATLIFF**

Bob Gatliff is head of the Marine, Coastal & Hydrocarbons Programme at the British Geological Survey, and is based in Edinburgh

The high seas

The movement of the ocean

The vast expanses of water held in the world's oceans are constantly on the move, forming columns of hot and cold moving water which circulate around the globe. There is a myriad of reasons why these currents occur – however the simplest and most important driving factors are wind and the position of the continents. As an example, the trade winds in the South Atlantic blow in a counterclockwise circle, which in turn drives the water below them in the same circular motion, pushing the heated water at the equator down past Brazil, across to South Africa and then up towards the Gulf of Guinea, where it is channelled westward again. This type of current is known as a gyre.

The importance of these major surface currents to the world's climate is exemplified by the Gulf Stream, which makes northwest Europe considerably warmer than it should be geographically. The warmer water originating in the tropical Gulf of Mexico circulates northwards along the east coast of the United States and moves across the North Atlantic until it hits Ireland, where it splits in two. This warm water forces down the cold water it encounters around the UK, and warms the air above it, increasing Britain's average temperatures by around 5C compared to other countries of a similar latitude.

Tracking the currents

Studying ocean currents is never an easy task – electronic measuring instruments are expensive and prone to break down in the unforgiving waters. Sometimes, however, oceanographers are blessed with a stroke of luck. In January 1992, a Hong Kong ocean freighter ran into some nasty weather in the North Atlantic, causing one container holding 29,000 plastic bath toys (yellow ducks, red beavers, blue turtles and green frogs) to fall overboard. Ten months later, when little yellow ducks began to arrive on the Alaskan shore, oceanographers sensed an opportunity. Since then, this unusual flotsam has been followed as it travels the globe, riding the ocean currents before washing up in polar sea ice, in the Great Pacific Garbage Patch (a swirling vortex of man-made filth) and on beaches from Japan to the Hebrides.

Opposites attract

The Earth's magnetic field

The magnetic compass has long been the key tool in man's efforts to explore the Earth. During the 16th century, mariners believed that there was a magnetic mountain somewhere in the north that was the source of attraction for compasses. In 1600, Sir William Gilbert, Queen Elizabeth I's physician, suggested that the Earth itself was a giant magnet and that the force that directed the compass originated inside the Earth. Thus at the ends of the Earth – the North and South Poles – a magnetised needle would stand vertical.

Gilbert was bang on. Scientists now believe that oceans of iron-rich molten rock, or magma, are forced to spin around the outside of the Earth's hot liquid outer core by the turning of the globe on its axis. This spinning soup of metal contains electrical currents which are lined up in the direction of the axis on which they spin. So magnetic north is roughly coincident with one end of the axis, and magnetic south with the other. This process is called the dynamo effect and operates on much the same principle as that which turns a coil of electrified wire into an electromagnet.

But, as many an explorer found at their cost, magnetic north actually shifts location constantly and is not consistent with true north – the northern end of the axis on which the Earth spins. This is because the electrical currents within the Earth are affected by variations of activity within the liquid outer core.

Polarity shifting

As well as the regular difference between magnetic north and true north, a much bigger shift has been observed. The seams of metal within rocks formed from a molten state line up with the polarity of the Earth's magnetic field at the time of their solidification. Study of such 'magnetic fossils' indicates that the Earth's magnetic field reverses every quarter of a million years or so as the north and south magnetic poles switch. There is evidence to suggest that the magnetic field is currently weakening, and so we might be heading towards a reverse in polarity relatively soon.

Sculpting nature

The story of the Earth Art movement

In 1946, the French artist Yves Klein had a daydream. Lying on his back in the sand at Nice, he imagined signing the back of the sky and claiming it as his own. Such a grandiose gesture had its drawbacks. 'On that day,' he wrote, 'I began to hate the birds that flew back and forth across the sky, because they were trying to punch holes in my greatest and most beautiful work.'

The relationship between artists and the natural world has long consisted of equal parts religious awe, thoughtful respect, and relentless competition. But none have been so brazen in their attempts to bend nature to their desires as the members of the Earth Art (or Land Art) movement in the Sixties and Seventies. While Klein challenged the immutable colour of the sky with his intensely blue monochrome paintings, the Earth Artists would leave canvas and the insular galleries of the city far behind them, taking nature to task within nature, and making art out of the landscape itself. Sculpture would no longer be just about form, but about place as well.

The huge undeveloped spaces of the American interior, and the large untapped resources of American art foundations, made Earth Art primarily an American movement. Many of its practitioners seemed to harken to the pioneering machismo of the frontiersman. Artists such as Michael Heizer, Robert Smithson and Walter De Maria preferred to displace air, rock and water rather than describe them on a canvas. They dug trenches, blasted rockfaces and dug holes, and in the process turned the deserts of the southwestern United States into their gallery. De Maria's *Lightning Field* (1977) consists of 400 20ft-high stainless-steel posts arranged in a grid measuring one mile by one kilometre in the high desert of New Mexico. Michael Heizer's *Double Negative* (1969-70) consists of two 100ft-long, 50ft-deep cuts in the rock, facing each other across a canyon in Nevada, forming a negative sculpture, the construction of which required the removal of 240,000 tons of rock. *Double Negative* is slowly being eroded away by wind and rain, and many Earthworks now live in photographs alone. Nature has a habit of punching holes in even the most monumental of artists' works. GEORGE PENDLE

Five of the most extraordinary examples of Earth Art

Spiral Jetty by Robert Smithson (1970) A 1,500ft-long coil jutting into the Great Salt Lake in Utah, *Spiral Jetty* was built out of mud and basalt rocks during a drought and then submerged for three decades, becoming the most famous work of art that almost no one had ever seen until it re-emerged during another drought in 1999.

City by Michael Heizer (1972-present) Possibly the largest piece of contemporary art ever attempted, *City* is a collection of giant earth mounds and huge metal abstract shapes, echoing ancient Inca and Aztec buildings, in the middle of the Nevada desert. The life work of Michael Heizer, it has so far taken 36 years and more than $25 million to build. It is scheduled to be completed in 2010, curiously around the same time as James Turrell's similarly gargantuan *Roden Crater* (1972-present), an extinct volcano in Arizona.

The New York Earth Room by Walter De Maria (1977) While *Lightning Field* is De Maria's most famous work, his Earth Rooms, of which this is the only one still surviving, brought Earth Art into the city: 280,000lb of pungent brown earth have been loaded onto the second floor of an innocuous building in New York's Soho area, the result being unexpected and spectacular.

Sun Tunnels by Nancy Holt (1976) One of the few female practitioners of Earth Art in America, Holt made a simple yet remarkably effective installation in the Utah desert consisting of four giant concrete tubes laid out in an 'x' formation. The tubes are pierced in various places so that specific constellations can be viewed through them.

A Line Made by Walking by Richard Long (1967) Striking a more subtle note than the American Earth artists, the British artist Richard Long has throughout his career documented his own minimal interventions in the landscape. This photograph of flattened turf is one of many intentionally transient pieces he made simply by walking through different landscapes and documenting how the shadow of his presence marked the land. GEORGE PENDLE

The big freeze

Why the Earth experiences ice ages

Despite the all-too-evident lack of woolly mammoths and a decent amount of snow at Christmas, we are currently in the middle of an ice age. To geographers, an ice age is defined as a phase in which ice sheets form in the northern and southern hemispheres (such as those that exist today in the Antarctic and Greenland), but during these longer stretches there can be much colder periods, called glacials, and warmer periods such as the one we're in now, called interglacials. However, geologically speaking, ice caps are an anomaly. Over the past 4.5 billion years, the Earth has tended towards a climate in which warm mountaintops and tropics covering much of the globe have prevailed.

Why this fluctuation in temperatures occurs is still open to debate. We know that greenhouse gases play a major part, with carbon-dioxide levels dropping before a major ice age. Why this happens is anyone's guess – and everyone has guessed, with theories ranging from supervolcanos exploding to continents shifting to meteor impacts. Glaciations, on the other hand, seem to occur in line with the Earth's Milankovitch cycles. These cycles describe the effect the Earth's 'wobbly' rotation has on the planet's climate, in that the Earth's axis will tilt and its orbit around the Sun shift in irregular patterns. A larger tilt means the ice has less time to melt in the summer months, so it will expand rapidly during the winter.

The last major glacial period ended around 10,000 years ago, heralding the Holocene epoch and the explosion of human civilisation. During this glaciation, global sea levels dropped by 120 metres, exposing the land bridges that allowed humans to walk from Russia to America, as massive glaciers spread around northern Europe and huge beasts, such as 6ft tall sloths and beavers the size of bears, roamed the Earth. A recent article in the magazine *Nature* argued that we may have another 18,000 years before the next glacial rolls along – however, the onset of climate change may either bring it along much sooner if the oceans' currents change or take us out of this ice age forever.

Huronian (2.7-2.3 billion years ago) The first ice age we know of

Cryogenian (850-630 million years ago) Possibly the most severe ice age the Earth has experienced, with the Snowball Earth theory suggesting that the whole planet was covered in ice. The global cooling that followed led to an explosion of complex organisms during the Cambrian period

Andean-Saharan (460-430m years ago) A relatively minor ice age attacking the Gondwana supercontinent, forming glaciers over what is now the Andes and Sahara

Karoo (350-260m years ago) Polar ice caps form and glaciers develop throughout the southern hemisphere, again on Gondwana

Holarctic-Antarctic (2.5m years ago to present) Permanent ice sheets form in Antarctica and Greenland; ice covers 30% of the globe

What is...

A glacier

Wherever snow collects and compacts, turning to ice, a glacier will form, although we tend to think of glaciers as particularly large bodies of ice. As a glacier becomes heavier, the ice within it deforms and the glacier moves slowly downhill because of gravity. As the ice melts through friction and heat under pressure at the base of the glacier, it acts as a lubricant, helping the ice to slide at around 2-3m (6-10ft) per day. Of course where the gradient of the glacier is steepest, the speed of the ice flow will be at its greatest.

As ice moves it picks up rock debris, called moraine, which is produced through weathering and erosion. This moraine embedded in the glacier turns the whole body of ice into something similar to a giant piece of sandpaper which scours the landscape beneath the glacier, leaving polished, smooth areas and great striations, or scratches, in the rock. Through this slow process, glaciers have been responsible for shaping much of the world's mountainous regions.

Earth mysteries

The odd alignments which dot our landscapes

In 1894 the astronomer Sir Norman Lockyer suggested that the temples of Ancient Egypt and Greece were aligned astronomically, going on to observe, in 1906, that Stonehenge and other British monuments were also orientated towards solstices, equinoxes and other calendar-based rituals and celebrations. The world of archaeology derided Lockyer's ideas – how could the savages of prehistory have intended any such thing? – but other fringe figures pursued them.

In 1925 Alfred Watkins, a Hereford merchant, published *The Old Straight Track*, contending that a web of lines crossed the British landscape, linking cairns, mounds, stone circles, churches and other sites from antiquity. Watkins thought such lines, which he dubbed leys, were remnants of prehistoric trading routes, but his followers went further, declaring that leys are 'energy lines' which can be dowsed. The Earth, in short, has a perceivable electromagnetic pattern, as the Chinese geomancers of feng shui had long suggested. By the Sixties the hippy generation was finding leys everywhere, offering explanations from subterranean streams to Atlantis to UFO paths.

Academic archaeology harrumphed, but in subsequent years the champions of leys, Earth mysteries (a multidisciplined 'holistic' approach to the study of ancient sites started in the Seventies) and astroarchaeology have steadily gained ground. The alignments suggested by Lockyer and Watkins have been validated, in part, while a series of speculative bestsellers have popularised the idea that there is more to the ancient world than piles of stones erected by our rude forerunners. Though still resistant to the concept of 'leys', today's archaeological talk is full of 'ritual landscapes'.

Three contested alignments

The St Michael line

The most famous and preposterous alignment is perhaps the most convincing. It's an odd fact that the longest unbroken stretch of land in

southern England, stretching from St Michael's Mount in Cornwall to Hopton-on-Sea in Norfolk, coincides with both the May Day sunrise and with a series of important monuments. Glastonbury Tor, Avebury Circle, Bury St Edmunds Abbey and Royston Cave feature on a list that includes several St Michael's churches (hence the name). The sceptics' contention that any random line is likely to align a jumble of sites from different eras makes a point, but the probability of a random pattern here is mind-bogglingly low.

The Nazca lines

In 1939 pilots flying above the desert plain of southern Peru reported strange markings on the ground (pictured), marks that on investigation turned out to be huge pictures etched into the Earth – birds, insects, animals, labyrinths – all of them laid out in straight lines that extended for several miles. Moreover, the figures could only be seen from the air. The lines, made between 200BC and 700AD, became the subject of huge speculation, including the claim from Erich von Däniken that the area was a landing strip for alien airships. God was an astronaut! Subsequently it has been shown that the figures can be made with simple surveying equipment, with or without a primitive hot air balloon. Why are the figures there? Sacred paths, early landscape art or UFO guides – take your pick.

The Giza pyramids and Orion's Belt

In 1994 authors Robert Bauval and Adrian Geoffrey Gilbert argued in *The Orion Mystery* that the Great Pyramid and its two companions were a terrestrial replica of the three stars of Orion's Belt – hence their not-quite-in-line position. Moreover, the baffling 'ventilation shafts' of the Great Pyramid were aligned to the constellations of Orion and Sirius (Osiris and Isis, to the Egyptians). Most Egyptologists shuddered – here was another example of the 'pyramidiocy' that had gripped the 19th century – but Gilbert and Bauval's scholarly argument, far from being debunked, has won over several leading academics. **Neil Spencer**

Neil Spencer is the astrologer for The Observer

✳ **The insider: potholer**

Dave Nixon

The beauty of cave exploration is that you don't know what you're going to find. You have the sense of exploration that people in the 18th century must have felt going halfway across the world. Nowadays people have been to most places on the world's surface, but here, 20 miles from Sheffield, no one can tell me what's in between cave X and cave Y.

You get stories passed down in caving legend – for instance, of someone rumoured to know where there was a big cave but who died without passing it on. I know the Castleton area in the Peak District very well. There was a blockage that no one had managed to get past in the far reaches of Peak Cavern. It was beyond a flooded section of cave where you had to get all your diving gear on and swim through a 400m sump. Then we found an article in the Cambridge University library by a chap called Plumtree who had diarised a trip he'd made in 1793. All the flashing lights came on because we hadn't known about his route... and sure enough, it turned out to be a bypass for the sump. It took six years of digging and removing spoil to get to the blockage by this different route, then in 1999 – after a year of digging and wriggling through little boulder chokes – we were standing in this enormous cavern. We couldn't even see the roof with our powerful head torches on. We spent six days climbing bit by bit until we got to the top. It's 142m high – a monster – the largest natural shaft in the UK. We called it Titan.

I've had a few sticky situations. You commit yourself to going through a squeeze head-first and you can't turn round and you have to come back and all your clothes start rucking up and you get stuck. Once you're into the situation you can always start to panic and start doing irrational things. You've got to try and keep cool when your back's touching the roof, belly's touching the floor, sides are touching the sides and water's flowing over your ears. The theory is: if you've got in you must be able to get out. And the payoff is that through that little squeeze it might just get bigger, and you're off again. The glory is in squeezing through.

As schoolboys, two mates and I clubbed together to buy a guide book with descriptions of local caves. That fired our imaginations, so we got hold of boilersuits, helmets and torches and went to have a look. I've been hooked ever since.

Once you get to understand the geology, the hydrology and the speleology (the scientific study of caves), then you begin actively discovering new caves. It's like a puzzle. The things that create caves are water and great periods of time. Water seeps through the limestone and dissolves it and makes these paths. It can flow up or down or sideways. You proceed by climbing up things, diving through sumps, digging out boulders and trying to extend the caves. You can free-dive short sections underwater. The usual trick is to go feet first and try and feel if there's an air pocket. I wouldn't jump free-diving into a sump unless I was pretty sure it was less than 8ft long.

We've found 52,000-year-old bones in caves and places where no one's been for 220 years. Footprints, handprints and graffiti. There's a bit in Speedwell Cave where a miner had written 'A health to all miners and maintainers of mines' and signed it '20 October 1781' in fancy old-fashioned writing.

I enjoy being in the silence and the dark. When you're down there you're completely concentrating on what you're doing. All your thoughts and worries are left on the surface. I've not thought about the Freudian explanations of being in the womb much. The inquisitiveness is the thing – we humans like to poke our noses into new places.

I've been caving in Borneo a couple of times. In the tropics you get all sort of life underground – it's tremendous. You get spiders, centipedes, swifts and beetles, a whole array. You can be 4km into a cave and a bat will fly by or a snake jump out. If you're camping underground for days at a time, the 24-hour day goes out the window – it extends into 27 hours. Your eyes get used to very low levels of light. After four, five days underground, when you get out the greenness and the colours and the light and smells are so much more intense. You get an overpowering, brilliant smell of grass. I love it down there, but it's lovely coming out. **DAVE NIXON**

Living rock

Stalagmites and stalactites

Stalactites, the long finger-like calcite deposits hanging down from cave ceilings (and faulty plumbing), are formed when water, laden with carbon dioxide and calcium carbonate, drips through cracks in the cave roofs. As the water droplet hangs from the crack, exposed to the air, the carbon dioxide escapes (as it does when a bottle of fizzy drink is opened), and the calcium carbonate is left behind as a miniscule solid layer. This builds up, at a rate of around 40mm a year on average, as the layer is joined by more and more water droplets until eventually a long, tapering stalactite hangs down. As some of the droplets run down the growing stalactite and drop onto the floor, the calcium carbonate, along with any other mineral solutions, builds in a similar way from the floor up into a stalagmite. Often these two formations meet, forming imposing limestone columns. If you're still getting the two confused, just remember the old 'ants in the pants' joke: the mites go up and the tights go down...

The island from the deep

In 2002 a small volcanic island mysteriously appeared off the coast of Sicily. Caused by new seismic activity, which pushed part of a large submerged volcano (known as Empedocles) above water, the phenomenon nearly caused a diplomatic incident. Its last appearance in 1831, when the volcano erupted and formed a 4km island of ash and debris, had caused European powers to squabble over the ownership of this useless rock. The British named it Graham Bank; Naples sent ships to conquer it from the British and named it Ferdinandea; the French landed on it and christened it Ile Julia, and finally Spain declared it rightfully theirs. The storm continued for months until the island, perhaps bored of these diplomatic wranglings, slipped quietly below the waves in January 1832. Its recent re-ascension inflamed old arguments. Realising that it was soon to emerge, the Italians planted a flag underwater, only for the UK to yet again claim it as their own. With satisfying symmetry, the island duly sank once more.

The mysterious wandering rocks

The Racetrack Playa, a huge dried-out lake in the scorching wilderness of Death Valley, holds a geological puzzle. The massive boulders, weighing up to 320kg, which litter the Playa appear to be slowly moving through the dry mud, with trails snaking across the landscape, sometimes for more than 3km. Why this dynamic-traction phenomenon occurs has long been debated. No human or animal footprints surround these trails, and the Playa is remarkably flat, so gravity isn't to blame. Inventive theories have suggested ghosts, aliens with nothing better to do, demons (hence the Playa's nickname, the Devil's Racetrack) and subterranean magnetic forces. The truth may be more prosaic. Recent research – including the measurement of the trails of more than 160 sliding rocks – has found that the rains which hit the region once or twice a year may create a slick mud across which the stones can sail, pushed by whirling 'dust devils' and strong winds funnelled through the gap in the surrounding mountains.

Land ahoy!

How the continents got their names

North and South America The New World's name was first documented on Martin Waldseemüller's 1507 world map – considered America's birth certificate. But the naming of the continents is shrouded in controversy. The most popular potential root is the name of Amerigo Vespucci, the Italian explorer who charted the coastline of South America. From Americus, a Latinised version of his first name, came America. However, there are doubts surrounding this explanation. Why did cosmographers ignore the standard rule of naming of new lands: the use of the surnames of explorers and the first names of royalty? And why did they use a new Latinised name, Americus, when Vespucci himself had already adopted the name Albericus in previous writings?

One alternative theory has the New World named after Richard Ameryk, or Amerike (both Anglicised versions of Ap Maryke), the Bristol-based Welsh customs official who handed over vast sums of money to the explorer John Cabot (himself originally named Giovanni Caboto) on behalf of the king. Cabot used the money to discover North America (although he thought it was simply an island off the Chinese coast). As he'd named other islands after friends (and even one after his barber/surgeon), it is not unreasonable to suspect that Cabot named this particular one after the king's official. Although hard evidence is thin on the ground, support for the theory comes from a Bristol manuscript (now sadly lost) dating from 1497 – five years before Vespucci returned from his travels – stating that 'the land of America was found by the merchants of Bristowe' (referring to Cabot's voyage). If the name was indeed known in Bristol at this time, Vespucci's name couldn't have been its origin.

Africa The word comes from the Latin *Africa terra*, meaning 'land of the Afri' – a primitive tribe which populated the Mediterranean shores of North Africa, near Carthage (in modern-day Tunisia). The Afris' name is thought to derive from the Berber word *ifri*, or cave. Although the Roman name originally applied only to

Tunisia, it came to mean an area finally encompassing the whole landmass as the Europeans' knowledge of the continent blossomed during the Middle Ages.

Arctic and Antarctic The Arctic was named after the constellation Ursa Major (the Great Bear) – or *arktikos* in Greek – which is only visible in the northern hemisphere. Antarctic is derived from the Greek *antarktikos*, which means literally 'opposite the Arctic'.

Asia It's unclear how the vast continent of Asia got its name, although the Hittite word *Assuwa* originally referred to the east coast of the Aegean Sea (now Turkey). *Assuwa* either has its roots in the old Aegean word *asis*, meaning muddy and silty (describing the Aegean shoreline), or in the Semitic *asu*, meaning rising (as in 'land of the rising sun'). The Ancient Greeks began using the word Asia to refer to the whole of Anatolia (the peninsula sandwiched between the Aegean and Black Sea), and as they and others became aware of the vast lands further east, the name came to mean the whole continent. The word's original meaning survives in Asia Minor, which still refers specifically to Anatolia.

Australasia *Australis* is the Latin word for 'of the south' and was used in the naming of the mythical *Terra Australis Incognita* (literally 'unknown southern land'), a huge continent geographers believed lay in the southern hemisphere. European explorers, on discovering a vast antipodean landmass, believed they had found this fantastical land, and it quickly became known as simply Australia.

Europe In Ancient Greek mythology, Europa was a Phoenician princess whom Zeus, disguised as a majestic white bull, abducted and carried over the Mediterranean to Crete. The Greeks came to label the whole of mainland Greece 'Europa', ostensibly after the mythical princess. However, the actual source of Europe's name is more hotly contested. Most believe the word stems from the Greek root *eur*, meaning broad, coupled with *ops*, meaning face. However some now believe that Europe may stem from the Semitic *ereb*, meaning setting (as opposed to Asia's *asu*) and referring to the land of the setting sun to the west.

James Hutton

(b. 3 June 1726; d. 26 March 1797)
Scottish geologist

Before James Hutton's groundbreaking *Theory of the Earth* was published in 1785, the prevailing belief among geologists was that the Earth had come into being on 22 October 4004BC, around the time of a great flood. In the decades that followed, the scientific community gradually accepted Hutton's theories, viewing the planet's creation as having taken more time than the Bible suggested.

> ❝ What more can we require? Nothing but time.
>
> James Hutton

Hutton's theories were an enormous imaginative leap at the time. Observing the sedimentary layers in cliff faces near his Edinburgh home, Hutton reasoned that they could only have formed after millions of years of incredible force and vast environmental change – in no way could they have been laid down in just 5,500 years. Instead, he argued, the Earth is in perpetual flux, and a hot, lava-like core is the driving force behind this great process. He argued that the geological forces at work today are exactly the same as those which shaped the world in the past – a theory known as uniformitarianism.

As well as brief stints as both a doctor and a farmer (he introduced innovative farming and husbandry techniques to Britain, picked up while living in Flanders), Hutton produced a great body of work, which he collected and published in 1794 as *An Investigation of the Principles of Knowledge and of the Progress of Reason, from Sense to Science and Philosophy*. His prose, however, was obscure and dense and so, combined with the inevitable religious backlash provoked by his theory, his work was unappreciated during his lifetime. It wasn't until two of Hutton's disciples, John Playfair and later Charles Lyell, developed and restated his ideas in the early 1800s that he finally found an audience – particularly with Darwin, who needed Hutton's age-old Earth to give his animals time to evolve.

'Let's drink to the hard-working people / Let's think of the lowly of birth / Spare a thought for the rag-taggy people / Let's drink to the salt of the Earth'
'Salt of the Earth' by the Rolling Stones (1968)

'Voices, another sound, can you hear me now? / This is planet Earth / You're looking at planet Earth'
'Planet Earth' by Duran Duran (1981)

'Hello Earth / Hello Earth / With just one hand held up high / I can blot you out / Out of sight'
'Hello Earth' by Kate Bush (1985)

'When she's on her best behaviour / Don't be tempted by her favours / Never turn your back on Mother Earth'
'Never Turn Your Back On Mother Earth' by Martin Gore (1989)

'And the army ants / They leave nothin' but the bones / And the Earth died screaming / While I lay dreaming of you'
'Earth Died Screaming' by Tom Waits (1992)

'Sweet change if anybody's listening? / Emergency on planet Earth / Is that life that I am witnessing?'
'Emergency on Planet Earth' by Jamiroquai (1993)

'What about sunrise / What about rain / What about all the things / That you said we were to gain...'
'The Earth Song' by Michael Jackson (1995)

'And they go on as the sacrifice grows / We're living on ground zero – fire! / This Island Earth!'
'This Island Earth' by the Misfits (1997)

'So don't rely on the stars above / Screw the universe / You'd better try to live your life on Earth'
'Life on Earth' by the Divine Comedy (1998)

'We are the Earth intruders / We are the sharp shooters / Flock of parashooters / Necessary voodoo'
'Earth Intruders' by Björk (2007)

On top of the world

How we came to love mountains

Three centuries ago, risking one's life to climb a mountain would have been considered tantamount to lunacy. The notion barely existed, indeed, that wild landscape might hold any sort of appeal. To the orthodox 17th- and early 18th-century imagination, natural scenery was appreciated largely for the extent to which it spoke of agricultural fecundity. Meadows, orchards, grazing fields, the rich sillion of crop lands – these were the ideal components of a landscape. Tamed landscapes, in other words. Mountains, nature's roughest productions, were not only agriculturally intractable, they were also aesthetically repellent: it was felt that their irregular and gargantuan outlines upset the natural spirit-level of the mind. The politer inhabitants of the 17th century referred to mountains disapprovingly as 'deserts'; they were also castigated as 'boils' on the earth's complexion, 'warts', 'wens', 'excrescences' and even, with their labial ridges and vaginal valleys, 'Nature's pudenda'.

Moreover, mountains were dangerous places to be. It was believed that avalanches could be triggered by stimuli as light as a cough or the footfall of a beetle. Or you might fall between the blue jaws of a crevasse, to be regurgitated years later by the glacier, pulped and rigid. Or you might encounter a god, demi-god, or monster angry at having their territory trespassed upon – for mountains were conventionally the habitat of the supernatural and the hostile. Go around mountains by all means, it was thought, along their flanks or between them if absolutely necessary but certainly not up them.

During the second half of the 1700s, however, people started for the first time to travel to mountains out of a spirit other than necessity, and a coherent sense began to develop of the splendour of mountainous landscape. The summit of Mont Blanc was reached in 1786, and mountaineering proper came into existence in the middle of the 1800s, induced by a commitment to science (in the sport's adolescence, no respectable mountaineer would scale a peak without at the very least boiling a thermometer on the summit) but very definitely born of beauty.

The complex aesthetics of ice, sunlight, rock, height, angles and air – what John Ruskin called the 'endless perspicuity of space; the unfatigued veracity of eternal light' – were to the later 19th-century mind unquestionably marvellous. Mountains began to exert a considerable and often fatal power of attraction on the human mind. 'The effect of this strange Matterhorn upon the imagination is indeed so great,' Ruskin could claim proudly of his favourite mountain in 1862, 'that even the gravest philosophers cannot resist it.' Three years later the Matterhorn was climbed for the first time; four of the successful summiteers fell to their deaths during the descent.

By the end of the century the alpine peaks had all been climbed and almost all the alpine passes mapped. The so-called Golden Age of mountaineering had come to an end. Europe was considered by many to be passé, and mountaineers began to turn their attention to the Greater Ranges, where they exposed themselves to extreme hardship and even greater risks in their bids to reach the summits of Caucasian, Andean and Himalayan mountains – Ushba, Popocatépel, Nanga Parbat, Chimborazo, or Kazbek, where Vulcan was said to have chained and bolted Prometheus to the rock. Everest (pictured), the highest and most imaginatively potent of all the world's peaks, came to enchant the British in particular, who considered it very much their mountain. Among the enchanted was George Mallory, whose death on Everest's shoulder in 1924 shocked and thrilled the nation.

In a little over two centuries, then, a tremendous revolution of perception occurred in the west concerning mountains. The qualities for which they were once reviled – steepness, desolation, perilousness – came to be numbered among their most prized aspects.

So drastic was this revolution that to contemplate it now is to be reminded of a truth about landscapes: that our responses to them are for the most part culturally devised. That is to say, when we look at a landscape, we do not see what is there, but largely what we think is there. We attribute qualities to a landscape which it does not intrinsically possess – savageness, for example, or bleakness – and we value it accordingly. ROBERT MACFARLANE

Dr Robert Macfarlane is a lecturer in English at Emmanuel College, Cambridge and the author of Mountains of the Mind: A History of a Fascination, *and most recently* The Wild Places

A mountain

Mountains make up 24% of the Earth's total landmass, rising up from every continent and in the process causing water to run off into countless rivers which shape the landscape by carving deep valleys and carrying away eroded material. The process of mountain building is called orogeny or orogenesis (from the Greek *oros*, meaning mountain, and *geneia*, meaning act of being born), and can occur in a number of ways – however, as with most geographical features, the basis for all these methods is the gradual shifting of the Earth's tectonic plates.

The Himalayas and Andes, among others, were formed by the collision of two continental plates – the Indian and Eurasian in the case of the Himalayas, and the Nazca and the South American in the case of the Andes. As these huge landmasses collide, one is pushed under the other, forcing the upper plate to fold and push up. As the plates continue to drive into each other, the nascent mountains are forced ever upwards, shaped into peaks by glacial and wind erosion, until eventually this general erosion takes over and the mountains shrink back (the Himalayas are still relatively young, and are growing a few centimetres a year). Uluru, aka Ayers Rock, in Australia is the remnant of a mountain range which has been eroded, leaving a stunning red sandstone monolith.

Other mountains are formed through volcanic forces: as the plates pull apart or pile into each other, magma (molten rock) can rush to the surface, quickly cooling to form huge igneous mountains. Mount Fuji in Japan (pictured) and Mount Kilimanjaro in Tanzania are examples of such stratovolcanos – composite volcanos that grow with each eruption as layers of emitted lava, ash and cinders pile on top of each other.

Climb every mountain...

How the heights of peaks are measured

Before the Global Positioning System (GPS) was developed, cartographers worked out the heights of mountains using trigonometry, measuring angles with a theodolite (pictured). By standing a known distance from a mountain and working out the vertical angle to the summit, you can calculate the mountain's height. In the 19th century, British surveyors conducting the Great Trigonometrical Survey of India measured the height of Kangchenjunga – the world's third-tallest mountain – from the modern-day town of Darjeeling. They calculated that it stood 28,176ft tall – just 7ft off today's height. Impressive considering that some of their readings were taken from 160 miles away. In 1856 they calculated the height of an even taller Himalayan mountain nearby – Peak XV, as it was known – as 29,002ft and named it after the former head of the survey, Sir George Everest.

In 1999, climbers used GPS to get a revised height of Mount Everest. They carried a receiver to the top, while two others simultaneously took altitude measurements near base camp at 18,000ft and on the South Col, a 26,000ft saddle a mile from the summit, allowing a reliable determination of the altitude and position of the world's highest mountain. Although GPS is highly effective, it has so far been impossible to get a conclusive measurement, as all estimates have measured the height of the snow pack on top of the summit, not the summit itself, and no one knows how deep the snow is. Most recent estimates put the mountain at 29,035ft.

The five highest mountains on Earth

	Mountain	Range	Country	Height in feet
1	Everest	Himalayas	Nepal/Tibet	29,035
2	K2 / Godwin Austen	Karakoram	Kashmir (Pakistan)	28,250
3	Kangchenjunga	Himalayas	India/Nepal	28,169
4	Lhotse	Himalayas	Nepal/Tibet	27,940
5	Makalu	Himalayas	Nepal/Tibet	27,766

Clocking on

A brief history of time (zones)

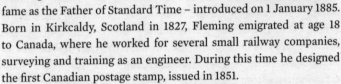

One of the foremost railway engineers of his age, Sir Sandford Fleming would achieve lasting fame as the Father of Standard Time – introduced on 1 January 1885. Born in Kirkcaldy, Scotland in 1827, Fleming emigrated at age 18 to Canada, where he worked for several small railway companies, surveying and training as an engineer. During this time he designed the first Canadian postage stamp, issued in 1851.

In 1863 Fleming was appointed chief engineer of the Intercontinental Railway, which connected New Brunswick and Nova Scotia to central Canada. He was also the first person to draw up plans for a coast-to-coast railway line across British North America, and in 1871 he was made director of the Canadian Pacific Railway Company, responsible for establishing a railway that would span the country from the Pacific to the Atlantic, crossing the Rockies.

> 66 *The only reason for time is so that everything doesn't happen at once.*
>
> Albert Einstein

It was during his travels that Fleming had the idea for a standard, universal system of time zones. Until then, time was locally based and measured by the Sun – noon being when the Sun stood exactly overhead, this was the way clocks were set all over the world. With the introduction of railways, this method became highly confusing and inefficient. It meant that if you travelled by train, at every stop along the way you would have to constantly reset your timepiece.

Fleming's idea was to divide the globe into 24 time zones, each of which is 15 degrees of longitude wide and corresponds to one hour of time. Within a zone, all clocks are set to the same local time, but differ by one hour from those in the neighbouring zones. At the International Prime Meridian Conference in October 1884, the local time at the Royal Greenwich Observatory, England was chosen as the standard, leading to the widespread use of Greenwich Mean Time (GMT) in order to set local clocks. This location was chosen because by 1884 two-thirds of all maps were using it as their prime meridian.

Where on Earth are we?

An introduction to longitude and latitude

Any location on Earth can be described by two numbers, or coordinates, which give its latitude and longitude. These mysterious numbers are in fact two angles, measured in degrees (°), minutes of arc (') and seconds of arc (") from two points: the equator and the Greenwich meridian. One degree contains 60 minutes of arc, and one minute contains 60 seconds of arc. On a globe of the Earth, lines (or parallels) of latitude appear as circles of different sizes above and below the equator – zero degrees latitude. Meanwhile lines (or meridians) of constant longitude extend from pole to pole like the segment boundaries on a peeled orange.

> **❝** *There isn't a Parallel of Latitude but thinks it would have been the Equator if it had had its rights.*
>
> Mark Twain

During the 17th century, accurately determining longitude at sea was an impossible task, and as a result of not knowing their true location, ships often ran aground, incurring the loss of many lives. In 1714, the British government offered a prize of £20,000 to anyone who could solve the problem and determine longitude to within half a degree. The challenge was taken up by John Harrison, a working-class joiner from Lincolnshire, who used his knowledge of mechanics to solve the problem.

As 15° of longitude is equal to one hour's time difference, Harrison reasoned that you could measure longitude by keeping accurate time. If you compare your local time with that at a fixed reference point (Greenwich), you can work out how far east or west of that point you are. For example, if it is midday in Greenwich but 10am where you are, you know that you are 30° west.

However, keeping accurate time at sea was extremely difficult, so Harrison set out to produce a clock that would not be affected by bad weather, the ship's movement and fluctuating temperatures. He produced a series of accurate clocks – H1, H2 and H3 – but they were still not quite good enough. So Harrison abandoned his earlier designs and worked on an adaptation of a pocket watch – known as H4 – which finally claimed the longitude prize.

Stairway to heaven

Five sacred mountains

1 Mount Kailish, Tibet

A towering 22,000ft pyramid of black rock with a perpetually snow-capped peak, Tibet's Mt Kailish has a reputation to fit its remarkable appearance. Four different faiths – Hindu, Jain, Buddhism and Bon (the pre-Buddhist religion of Tibet) – revere the mountain as the *axis mundi*, the centre of the world, and have populated it with a host of deities. For Hindus it is the abode of the Lord Shiva. For Jains it is where their faith's founder, Rishaba, attained enlightenment. For the Bons it is the seat of the sky goddess Sipaimen. For Buddhists it is the home of the Buddha Demchog and his consort. Furthermore, Kailish is the source of four major rivers, including the Indus, and overlooks a pair of magical lakes. Though it has never been climbed – its sanctity puts it off limits to mountaineers – Kailish is a place of pilgrimage, with pilgrims called to circumambulate the remote mountain, preferably in a single breathtaking day.

2 Uluru/Ayers Rock, Australia

A vast outcrop of ancient sand-stone in the centre of the Austral-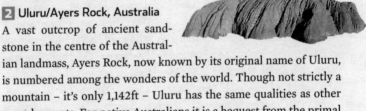
ian landmass, Ayers Rock, now known by its original name of Uluru, is numbered among the wonders of the world. Though not strictly a mountain – it's only 1,142ft – Uluru has the same qualities as other sacred mounts. For native Australians it is a bequest from the primal 'Dreamtime' and the residence of numerous divine beings: its distinctive indentations were made by the throwing stick of the lizard Tatji. Numerous rock and cave paintings attest to Uluru's place in local mythology. The rock's celebrated changes of colour are rooted in its unusual geology, which alongside grey sandstone includes feldspar, quartz and red iron oxide. The rock is estimated to have been on the seabed some 800m years ago, with surrounding sedentary deposits subsequently eroded away.

3 Machu Picchu, Peru

Some sacred mountains are too holy to climb, others are capped with temples and monasteries, or in the case of Machu Picchu, a small city. Erected by the Incas in the Middle Ages, Machu Picchu (meaning Old Peak in Quechan) was unknown until 1911, when its ruins were uncovered by US archaeologist Hiram Bingham. Although it is 9,000ft up, the Andean mountaintop site had springs, agricultural terraces, houses, temples, cemeteries and – probably the site's raison d'être – an astronomical observatory. At the spring and autumn equinoxes, the Sun appears to be standing still above a post at the centre of Machu Picchu's observatory, while at the summer solstice the Sun disappears behind Pumasillo (meaning Puma's Claw), one of several nearby sacred peaks – Wayna Picchu (or Young Peak) features another observatory in a cave.

4 Mount Fuji, Japan

Sacred to the Japanese Shinto religion and Buddhism, Fuji has also become a potent national symbol, thanks in part to the acclaimed *36 Views of Mount Fuji* series painted by Hokusai in the early 19th century. That the perfectly conical summit is sometimes visible from Tokyo has also helped its cause. At 12,388ft, Fuji is Japan's tallest peak, though it's a volcano rather than a mountain, and a young one at that – perhaps a mere 10,000 years old. It last erupted in 1702. Predictably it is the home of a fire god, but also the dwelling place of a Shinto goddess and the Buddha Dyichi Nyorai. It has long been a place of pilgrimage, though to judge by the debris left by the 40,000 people who climb it each year, ideas of sanctity have changed for the worse.

5 Croagh Patrick, Ireland

'The holiest mountain in Ireland', the County Mayo peak (2,510ft), aka the Reek, is visited by tens of thousands of pilgrims on Reek Sunday, the last Sunday in July. These days the ascent is usually taken as an act of Catholic penance, with many pilgrims climbing in bare feet or on their knees, but the quartz-tipped mountain has never lost its association with the mother goddess whom St Patrick is said to have cast out, along with serpents and dragons. Until the mid 19th century, only barren women were permitted to climb the last 250m of scree to the summit. The annual harvest festivities held at the foot of Croagh Patrick may have helped their search for fertility – William Thackeray describes a visit in 1840 where feasting, dancing and merry-making were happily combined. **NEIL SPENCER**

Charles Lyell

(b. 14 November 1797; d. 22 February 1875)
Scottish geologist

Sir Charles Lyell was the man who brought James Hutton's revolutionary geological ideas to the masses, bolstering them with hard evidence. It was Lyell's *Principles of Geology* that Darwin took on the Beagle voyage and which he later claimed 'altered the whole tone of one's mind, and therefore... when seeing a thing never seen by Lyell, one yet saw it through his eyes'. With this 1830 tome Lyell was one of the first to carry out a detailed examination of the Earth's past using knowledge of present geological processes – the basic tenet of uniformitarianism.

> ❝ *The existing causes of change have operated with absolute uniformity from all eternity.*
>
> Charles Lyell

Rather than adhering to the prevailing theory of catastrophism, which stated that the Earth was essentially stable but for the odd cataclysmic event such as an earthquake or flood, Lyell argued that the Earth is transformed by imperceptibly slow changes. Valleys are formed by rivers eroding away the land and mountains are created by molten rock pushing up from below.

Not that this theory was perfect. So staunchly did Lyell deny that catastrophes had any bearing on the Earth that he would never have accepted some of today's geological truths: that the early Earth's composition was shaped by cosmic debris pummelling it over hundreds of millions of years, or that the Earth's geography and biology were profoundly changed by the K-T meteor impact 65 million years ago. However, uniformitarianism gave geologists a framework they could work with: ie to find out how volcanos have developed, just go and study a volcano today. In 1848 Lyell was awarded a knighthood for his contribution to science, and was laid to rest alongside Isaac Newton in Westminster Abbey. Craters on both the Moon and Mars bear Lyell's name.

Getting on a bit

How we know the age of the Earth

Creationists fixed the Earth's birthday at 22 October 4004BC; Hindus believe the Earth, and the universe in general, is subject to cycles of birth, death and rebirth billions of years long, while Chinese traditional religion holds that these cycles last 23 million years. It took the rapid advance of geology in the late 18th and early 19th centuries to blow apart biblical theory and begin an investigation into the true age of the Earth that would last more than a century.

> **"** *In science there is only physics; all the rest is stamp collecting.*
>
> Ernest Rutherford

In 1779 the French naturalist Comte du Buffon created a mini-Earth, resembling the planet in composition, to hazard arguably the first scientific guess at our planet's lifespan. He measured how fast his model cooled, and scaled up the figures to apply to a planet-sized rock, concluding that it was 75,000 years old. But within 80 years this figure had been inflated to anywhere between 24m and 400m years.

However, to the biologists only just beginning to come to terms with the sheer scale of time necessary for evolution to take place based on Darwin's theories, even this monumental time period seemed too short. Predictions came thick and fast, each packaged with a weighty paper explaining how this new theory was better than any that had come before, yet still by the turn of the 20th century the geology community's best guess was 100m years.

Then came New Zealand physicist Ernest Rutherford and radiometric dating. Knowing the half-life (the length of time it takes for a radioactive substance to lose half its mass as a decay product) of certain elements, Rutherford calculated that the age of a rock could be discovered simply by measuring the concentration of helium, which is a by-product of the decay of radium, within it. This test was developed and refined (radium and helium were substituted for uranium and lead, which in modern times can be substituted for any number of elements) until in 1956, using methods developed by Rutherford, scientists estimated the age of the Earth to be roughly 4.55 billion years – an age which has survived intense scientific scrutiny to this day.

The ages of the Earth

Stewarded by the International Commission on Stratigraphy, the geological timescale is part of the international language of geology, helping to codify and quantify billions of years into a simple set of geological 'dynasties', all labelled with words derived from Greek or from places where they were first recognised (for example, Devonian from Devon). The largest category is the eon, which splits the Earth's lifespan into three distinct phases – the first (the Archean) describes an interval with only bacteria living on Earth, during the second free oxygen appeared in the atmosphere, while the third saw an explosion in complex life.

The divisions between the eons, eras, periods and epochs tend to be marked at changes such as biological extinctions. The boundaries between the eras are mostly formed by major extinctions events, such as the K-T which killed off the dinosaurs between the Mesozoic and Cenozoic eras 65 million years ago, or the P-T event which wiped out 90% of species on Earth at the end of the Paleozoic era. The boundaries between periods tend to denote more minor extinctions or significant changes in the rock strata, which often reflect climate changes (such as the global refrigeration at the beginning of the Quaternary period). Epochs reflect lesser changes – the modern Holocene epoch began when the ice last retreated, while the beginning of the Eocene marks an intense pulse of global warming.

Age	Eon	Era	Period	
	Phanerozoic (Meaning 'Visible life')	Cenozoic (Meaning 'New life')	Quaternary	
			Neogene	
			Paleogene	
100		Mesozoic (Meaning 'Middle animals')	Cretaceous	From the Latin *creta*, meaning chalk, due to large chalk deposits from this period
			Jurassic	Comes from the Jura mountains between France and Switzerland
200			Triassic	Named after the three layers – red beds, chalk and black shales – found from this period

(Millions of years)

Age	Eon	Era	Period	
300	Phanerozoic (Meaning 'Visible life')	Paleozoic (Meaning 'Ancient life')	Permian	Named after Perm, in the Urals
			Carboniferous	Named for the massive coalbeds found in Western Europe
			Devonian	Named after Devon, as rocks from this period were studied in Exmoor
400			Silurian	These take their name from Welsh tribes, or Wales itself (Cambria is the classical name for Wales), as studies into rocks from these periods were done in Wales
			Ordovician	
500			Cambrian	
	Proterozoic (Meaning 'Earliest life')	Neo-proterozoic	Ediacaran	
			Cryogenian	From the Greek *cryos*, meaning ice, and *genesis* (birth), as this period is characterised by a severe ice age
1,000			Tonian	
		Meso-proterozoic	Stenian	
			Ectasian	
1,500			Calymmian	
		Paleo-proterozoic	Statherian	From the Greek *statheros*, meaning stable, as continents became stable landmasses in this period
			Orosirian	From the Greek *orosira*, meaning mountain range, as much orogeny, or mountain forming, took place
2,000			Rhyacian	From the Greek *rhyax*, meaning lava flow, as this was a period of massive volcanic activity
			Siderian	From the Greek *sideros*, meaning iron, as banded iron formations have been found from this time
2,500	Archean (Meaning 'Ancient things')	Neoarchean		
		Mesoarchean		
3,000		Eoarchean		
		Paleoarchean		
4,000	Hadean			Named after the Greek underworld of Hades, or hell
4,600				

(Millions of years)

Miguel Rodriguez

Every day I get up at 5am and walk up from the fringes of town to the market. There I buy dynamite and coca leaves and head to the entrance of the mine to meet the other members of my *cooperacíon*. We don boilersuits and helmets with torches fixed on – the helmets are pretty flimsy, from the Nineties – and we then walk and crawl deep into Cerro Rico (or Rich Mountain). I come out 12 hours later.

> **❝** *It is only because miners sweat their guts out that superior persons can remain superior.*
>
> George Orwell

No food, just a few 20-minute stops for rest – we chew the coca leaves all day and they stop us feeling hungry and give us energy to work.

My immediate family has been mining in Cerro Rico, Bolivia for seven generations; my people have been mining here for 20 generations. We were living at the top of the world in the high Andes when the Spanish came in the 16th century. They realised that our mountain was full of silver, and they set us to work on the mountain. We have a museum in town that tells the story; there are coins from the 16th century. These coins were taken across the continent and then taken by ship from Venezuela back to Europe. Pirates hung around the Caribbean in order to nab the silver from the ships. The ships that made it delivered their silver to the king of Spain. Back in those days Potosí was one of the four biggest, wealthiest cities in the world, along with Seville, London and Paris. But the wealth didn't come to

us. At first my ancestors were paid a pittance, but then the Spaniards changed the system and used forced labour. We think 8 million Aymara and Quechua Indians have died in Cerro Rico in the last 500 years. We call the entrance the 'mouth of hell'.

These days we enter in teams and work the mine privately. We use picks, dynamite and metal trucks on wheels to remove the ore. It's pretty tough work, good exercise, and I sleep very well at night. We get a payment from private companies depending on how many trucks of ore we can remove. Much of the silver has gone, so we mine other things as well: iron, zinc, tin, lead, cadmium and chromium. The ore is smelted in factories outside.

Most miners don't work for more than 20 years – they're dead by then. I've been lucky, going in for 26 years, since I was 12. The most dangerous time is when we're blasting. After so much digging, the mountain is like a sponge. Sometimes the roof falls in and traps us, or even kills someone; sometimes pockets of poisonous gas are released. Several of my friends have died from this poisoning – I collapsed once from it and had to be dragged out by a friend. You make good friends when you work in the mine.

About 50 of us die every year. Sometimes we blast open the vein we're working on into a vein which other miners are working on. If we don't quickly agree on what's to happen, we will often start fighting the rival team to see who is going to get to carry on working there. Yes, people have died in these fights. The other big danger is silicosis. We don't have breathing equipment, so we inhale rock dust the whole time. Most miners have breathing problems. I have 40% silicosis. I only get a government pension when I get to 80% – I won't have much need for it by then though.

After work we drink El Puro (a 96% proof alcohol drink) and laugh and joke together before heading home for our daily meal. I hate the mine in a way, but it's the only place I can work. My son takes tourists round the mine, which is much better because he only spends five hours a day in it – much safer. I hope his son gets educated and finds a job in a building and not in the mine. It feeds us, but it's also eaten enough of my family already.

I can see Cerro Rico all the time I'm not in it. It's a pink cone visible from all over the town. **MIGUEL RODRIGUEZ**

Miguel Rodriguez is 38 and works in the silver mines of Potosí in Bolivia

Angry Earth

The five greatest natural disasters in history

1 Shaanxi earthquake, China (23 January 1556)

There have been earthquakes of greater magnitude, but the deadliest on record took place on the morning of 23 January 1566 in the Shaanxi province of central China. The death toll, an estimated 830,000, was so high due to population density and the fact that many people in the Loess Plateau area lived in artificial caves, or *yaodong*, which were wiped out by landslides. Many of the surrounding provinces were badly hit and deaths were recorded as far as 300 miles away from the Wei River Valley epicentre. In some counties, up to 60% of the population was said to have perished. Although facts and figures from that long ago tend to be unreliable, China's efficient bureaucracy was particularly good at keeping records – and it is generally agreed that this was history's most devastating earthquake.

2 Mount Tambora volcanic eruptions, Indonesia (April 1815)

We think of Krakatoa as the most dramatic volcanic event of modern times, but the eruption of its Indonesian neighbour Mount Tambora, nearly 70 years earlier, was four times more powerful and much deadlier. It measured seven on the Volcanic Explosivity Index, making it the largest eruption since 181AD. Of the 70,000 to 90,000 people who perished, about 10,000 were killed by pyroclastic flows (fast-moving hot gas and rock), which spread more than 12 miles from the summit. Others died as a result of post-eruption famine and disease. The explosion was heard 1,600 miles away, and ash carried for 800 miles. Vividly coloured sunsets were reported in London in the months that followed. Global climates were severely affected and 1816 – 'the year without a summer' – was the coldest on record in the northern hemisphere, causing crop failure throughout Europe and North America. It could be argued that the famines of the late 1810s, which claimed as many as 100,000 lives, were triggered by the Tambora eruption.

3 Yellow River flood, China (July-November 1931)

River flooding has posed a terrible problem in China over the millennia. The Yangtze has flooded more than 1,000 times in the last 2,000 years. But China's most catastrophic flood – and the world's deadliest natural disaster on record (not counting pandemics) – occurred in 1931 when the banks of the Hwang Ho, or Yellow River, burst, completely flooding 88,000 sq km of land. As many as 3.7 million people drowned or perished as a result of ensuing disease, famine and drought. The river, known abroad as 'China's sorrow', had caused nearly 2m deaths by flooding just a few decades earlier, in 1887, and when it flooded again in 1938, 1m people died. Its high silt content – as much as 60% by weight in some stretches – generates vast quantities of yellow mud, which can block the river's progress. China is currently building 27 dams in the hope that the source of its sorrow can finally be controlled.

4 Bhola cyclone, Bangladesh (12 November 1970)

The coast of the Bay of Bengal is particularly vulnerable to tropical storms, and in November 1970, the deadliest hurricane on record struck East Pakistan (now Bangladesh). The official death toll was 224,000 but some estimates put it as high as 500,000. A depression moving north through the Bay of Bengal intensified over four days into a Category 3 hurricane and struck land on the evening of 12 November. Many islands in the Ganges delta were completely devastated by the storm surge, which in the worst-hit city, Thana, killed more than 45% of the population of 167,000. Crops were destroyed by floods, and 3.6m people were directly affected by the storm, which cost an estimated $86.4m (£43.7m). It also had historical consequences. The inadequate response to the disaster by the government in West Pakistan only fuelled the desire for independence in East Pakistan, which a year later became Bangladesh.

5 Indian Ocean tsunami (26 December 2004)

The earthquake that took place off the west coast of Sumatra on Boxing Day 2004 released the energy of 23,000 Hiroshima-type atomic bombs, unleashing waves that sped across the Indian Ocean at the speed of a jumbo jet. Some of the waves were up to 30 metres high when they struck land. By the end of the day, more than 225,000 people were dead in 11 countries (some believe the death toll stretched to 350,000). Indonesia, Sri Lanka, India and Thailand were the worst hit, although fatalities were also reported 3,000 miles away, on the coasts of Kenya and Somalia. A further 40,000 people were never found, according to a UN report. **KILLIAN FOX**

Liquid gold

The story of oil

Oil didn't become the world's predominant fuel source until the mid-20th century, but it has been exploited for more than four millennia. Ancient Persians used it for medicinal and lighting purposes. Oil wells existed in China in the 4th century and the Middle Eastern petroleum industry was up and running by the 8th century, producing tar for roads and, later, kerosene and naphtha. Oil sands were mined in Alsace from 1745; the first refinery was built there in 1857. The first North American oil well was drilled in Ontario a year later, and as breakthroughs were made in refining during the late 1800s, interest in the oil industry spread rapidly.

It wasn't until the rise of the internal combustion engine at the turn of the 20th century that oil became a precious commodity, although in spite of the early-century oil booms, coal remained the world's primary fuel until the Fifties. We now consume around 83 million barrels of oil per day. Our reliance on the commodity – the cause of international conflict – is becoming increasingly strained as world oil reserves threaten to run out before the end of this century.

What is oil?

The term has diverse meanings, but when we talk of oil as a fuel source, we are referring to crude oil, or petroleum, and its constituent parts, including petrol, diesel and natural gas. Crude oil is a thick, flammable, yellow-black mixture of gaseous, liquid and solid hydrocarbons. It is commonly found in porous rock formations in the Earth's crust. It is formed from the remains of prehistoric animal and plant life that settled in large quantities at the bottom of seas and lakes. Buried under layers of heavy sediment, this matter is compressed and heated over millions of years.

Crude oil is of limited use when it is extracted from the ground but it can be separated by distillation into its very useful components. These fuel our transport systems and houses, surface our roads, and produce the plastics we use in our day-to-day lives. **KILLIAN FOX**

Natural gas

The most popular fuel in the UK, gas provides around 23% of the world's energy. It is a combustible concoction of gases, with methane making up the vast majority and the hydrocarbons ethane, propane and butane forming most of the remainder (occasionally harmless odorants are added to make the gas smell like rotten eggs or boiled cabbage in an effort to prevent unwitting users from leaving the gas on and accidentally blowing their homes to smithereens).

The fuel is formed – like coal and oil – when plant and animal remains are submitted to the intense heat and pressure found below the Earth's crust over millions of years, after which it is trapped beneath the surface in huge natural gas 'fields', as well as above oil and coal deposits. It is natural gas that causes the fiery plumes above oil wells, as the gas is allowed to escape and ignite – a practice now banned in many countries due to both its wasting of a valuable resource and the associated environmental cost. Although the biggest gas source is the North Field, off the coast of Qatar, the largest producer is Russia, generating nearly a quarter of the world's supply.

Coal

The mineral that powered the Industrial Revolution still provides 40% of the world's electricity, and with China building two coal-powered generators a week, this dominance looks set to continue.

Made in ancient swamps, where plants encased in mud slowly formed the hard combustible rock, coal has different properties depending on the geological conditions in which it was produced. Lignite, or brown coal, and bituminous coal are the most common and are used in electric-power generation; anthracite is the purer black rock we use to heat our homes; peat, considered to be the first stage in coal development, is also often used as fuel.

Coal is also the most environmentally hazardous of all the fossil fuels. Not only are dangerous levels of carbon dioxide released when it's burned, but radioactive materials are also a by-product.

Alexander von Humboldt

(b. 14 September 1769; d. 6 May 1859)
German naturalist and explorer

Charles Darwin called him 'the greatest scientific traveller who ever lived', and Alexander von Humboldt's work is still commemorated in the names of seven towns, six geographical features, 12 plant and animal species and the field of Humboldtian science – a movement shaped by an understanding of the interconnectedness of nature

> ❝ *Alexander von Humboldt has done more for America than all its conquerors; he is the true discoverer of America.*
>
> Simón Bolívar

through precise measurement. While studying geology at the Freiberg Mining Academy, the Berlin-born Humboldt befriended George Forester, a scientific illustrator, and caught the travel bug as they hiked around Europe. By 27 he had resolved to explore the unknown geography and wildlife of Latin America.

On 5 June 1799 he set off focused on the flora, fauna and topography of the mysterious continent, mapping more than 1,700 miles of the Orinoco River and breaking altitude records while climbing Mount Chimborazo in the Andes (he reached 18,000ft). He mapped volcanos in Ecuador, charted ocean currents in Peru and took animal specimens in Cuba. He even found time to visit Thomas Jefferson in Washington DC, who later called Humboldt 'the most important scientist I have met'. Humboldt's impact on the region is profound – Venezuelan schoolchildren today are taught about the great Alejandro de Humboldt, who 'named all flowers and stones'.

After he returned to Berlin a hero in 1804, Humboldt dedicated 30 years to writing and publishing reports of his four-year adventure. After a brief trip around Russia, he set about creating his masterpiece: *Cosmos: A Sketch of the Physical Description of the Universe*. The first volume was published when he was 76 and sold out within two months – he died before the fifth volume was completed.

The planet's heart of gold

Researchers now believe that 99% of the Earth's gold – enough to pave the planet's surface to a depth of 1.5ft – has been hiding in the planet's core for the past 4.5 billion years. While the Earth was still a molten embryo, the siderophile (literally iron-loving) elements – those which form easy bonds with iron, including gold and platinum – were pulled into the Earth's iron-rich core while its surface was still an ocean of liquid magma. The Earth's surface was then bombarded with meteorites over billions of years, supplying us with the scarce gold deposits we have today.

Meteorites, which represent planetesimals (small bodies of gas and dust that eventually coalesce to form planets), contain very similar concentrations of most elements to those we find on Earth yet have far higher levels of these siderophile substances. Australian geologist Bernard Wood has used this fact to calculate that as much as 1.6 quadrillion tons of gold could lie at the Earth's core (while this may seem a lot, it is still just a tiny percentage of the core's overall mass – about one part per million), along with six times as much platinum. But before the prospector in you begins investing in shovels, it's worth remembering that the Earth's core can reach a temperature of 3,700C.

The 10 longest rivers on Earth

River	Country or region	Length in miles
1 Nile	Africa	4,160
2 Amazon	South America	4,000
3 Chang Jiang (Yangtze)	China	3,964
4 Huang He	China	3,395
5 Ob-Irtysh	Russia	3,362
6 Amur	NE Asia	2,744
7 Lena	Russia	2,734
8 Congo	Central Africa	2,718
9 Mackenzie	Canada	2,635
10 Mekong	SE Asia	2,600

Stones in your pockets

The metals and rocks in your mobile

'If you can't grow it, you have to mine it' is a favourite saying of geologists, but this simple fact can be easily forgotten as technology becomes ever more complex. Although the link between a mobile phone, for example, and the rocks, minerals and ores which make up the Earth may seem tenuous, it simply goes to illustrate how we all rely on what can be dug from the ground...

Acrylonitrile Butadiene Styrene/Polycarbonate alloy (ABS/PC) The production of 1kg of ABS – used in the plastic casings of most mobile phones – requires the equivalent of 2kg of oil. A light, inexpensive yet tough plastic, ABS is also used to make musical instruments, golf-club heads, Lego bricks and even tattoo ink. Polycarbonate has similar properties to Perspex (PMMA), yet is stronger and thus more expensive.

Copper A crucial component of the circuitry of any electronic device due to the fact that, as well as being malleable and ductile, it is a very good conductor of electricity. It is also one of the first metals used by man: there is evidence of copper jewellery dating back to 8700BC, and signs of copper smelting dating from 5000BC. Today Chile mines more than one-third of the world's supply.

Glass Stone Age man was the first to spot the possible uses of glass, employing obsidian, a natural volcanic glass, for their cutting tools. The ancient Mesopotamians were the first to create artificial glass, when sand found its way into kilns, creating highly prized glass beads. Today superheated silica is still the most common form of glass, which is used, among countless other applications, in your mobile-phone camera.

Aluminium Despite being the most abundant metal in the Earth's crust, pure aluminium wasn't produced until 1827. Aluminium is only found in nature as a compound such as bauxite, and with copper it is used as part of mobile-phone electronics (despite having around 65% the conductivity of copper, it is lighter and cheaper). China produces around one-fifth of the world's supply, with Russia, Canada and the USA close behind.

Iron Stainless steel, used as a rust-proof metal finish on many modern mobiles, is an alloy of iron, carbon and chromium. There is evidence of steel production in East Africa in the 12th century BC, however iron artefacts have been traced much further back. Probably sourced from meteorites (indeed, the word iron is thought to stem from an ancient root meaning 'the gods'), iron was used by the Egyptians more than 6,000 years ago.

Silicon Appears in both its original form, as a crucial component of the phone's microchip and liquid crystal display, and as silicon dioxide in the phone's circuitry. It is the second-most abundant element in the Earth's crust (making up about 25% of its mass) and is found in sand, quartz, flint, opal and amethyst.

Nickel Found in your mobile's microphone, it has been used since ancient times, yet the ores of nickel were usually confused with silver (much of today's silverware is actually made from nickel). In 1751 the German baron Axel Frederik Cronstedt was attempting to extract copper from a nickel-based mineral, kupfernickel (or 'the devil's copper'), when he instead obtained a white metal that he named nickel, meaning 'Old Nick', or Satan. Today 30% of the world's supply comes from the Sudbury region of Canada, an oval basin formed when a meteorite smashed into the Earth 1.85 billion years ago.

Tin One of the first metals known to man, tin is used as the solder holding together the electronic parts of the phone. It is commonly used for its anti-rust properties and, when the ancients alloyed it with copper, helped to usher in the Bronze Age. China again tops the list of world producers, with Indonesia close behind, though current estimates give us just 40 years before this supply runs out.

Lithium One of the few elements thought to have been created in the Big Bang and used as the electrolyte in most new mobile-phone batteries, lithium was also used in 19th-century medicine to treat gout, and today it is used in the treatment of bipolar disorder.

Cobalt Used to create the battery's cathode, cobalt is also the main component of vitamin B12 and for millennia has been used to dye glass and ceramics a rich blue colour. Cobalt-60, a radioactive cobalt isotope, is used in tiny amounts in radiotherapy.

Graphite Used as the anode in most Li-ion batteries, graphite is the most stable form of carbon, as well as the very highest grade of coal (although the fact that it is near impossible to ignite means its use as a fuel is limited).

Fiona Spence

The largest diamond ever found was the Cullinan diamond (pictured), discovered in 1902 in South Africa. It weighed 3,106 carats, which is 600g – about the size of a large mug. It was cut into nine important stones and 80-odd satellite stones. Two of the important ones are in the Crown Jewels and the Royal Sceptre. The company generously presented it to the royal family – there was schmoozing in diamonds even back then. A diamond has grains in it like a piece of wood, so if you get the cut wrong it can explode. It's said the diamond cleaver fainted from the pressure as he split the Cullinan in two.

Diamonds are special because they were formed before the dinosaurs were around, when the Earth was covered in volcanos. The tremendous heat and pressure turned carbon into diamond. Diamonds were found 5,000 years ago in the Golconda region of India, and because they were so hard they were worn by kings as amulets to ward off evil. The ancient Greeks thought they were 'splinters of the tears of the gods'. The first betrothal using a diamond ring was when the Archduke Maximilian of Austria presented one to Mary of Burgundy in 1477. Rubies and emeralds have been fashionable for longer than diamonds – engagement rings were made of gold and opals because only kings, queens and tycoons could afford diamonds. Then in the 1870s the Kimberley mine in South Africa was discovered. There was a diamond rush making them available to a wider range of people and became the standard engagement ring.

The average price of a piece of Graff jewellery is around £250,000. The most expensive is in the tens of millions. We recently acquired a purplish-red diamond. There are only six in the world, so they have a huge premium – they go for more than $1 million a carat. In 2006 up pops the 15th-largest diamond of all time in Lesotho. We got hold of that. At 603 carats it had a strange inclusion in the middle, so using the newest technology and software to scan it and work out how best to cut the stone, they ended up with 26 diamonds – each one is a D flawless. Then a few months ago, at the same mine, someone discovered the 18th-largest of all time. The coincidence of finding these two stones in such a short period of time is incredible.

The price of diamonds has never fallen. De Beers had a huge control over the supply. Clients are called 'sight holders' because up until recently De Beers would show you a load of diamonds without allowing you to touch or choose and say: 'We'll give you this for your $2 million.' But there's been a shift in power in the last seven years.

Artificial diamonds came in five to 10 years ago. They have tried to recreate the heat and pressure of volcanic activity in a factory, and now they're beginning to get it right. De Beers used to make industrial diamonds for a huge number of applications: diamond drill bits, windows in space rockets, record styluses, transatlantic cables.

The fact that they're portable makes diamonds a target for criminals. You have a lot of security, but we also know that each of our diamonds has the Graff logo lasered on, so it would have to be an unscrupulous trader who'd buy or sell one. You have certificates of provenance for diamonds, as with works of art. But there is a black market. After the attempted diamond robbery at the Millennium Dome the gems were switched for replicas – but I can guarantee that up until then they were the genuine article.

How to buy a diamond

When you buy a diamond you've got to look for the four Cs: the cut, the colour, the clarity and the carat (weight). The size can matter, but it loses value if it's a low colour and has lots of inclusions: when diamonds are first formed there are sometimes carbon deposits left like bubbles, hence the black spots in the diamond which are called inclusions. A perfectly clean diamond is called a D-flawless diamond. In the Forties and the Fifties the most common cut was a rose cut, then in the Sixties some mathematicians came up with the 'brilliant cut', which maximises the number of facets, the amount of reflection and refraction, and the light. FIONA SPENCE

Fiona Spence works for the diamond jeweller Graff, which is involved in all stages of diamonds from mining to cutting, polishing and design

An earthquake

The Earth produces cataclysmic rumbles thousands of times every day. Earthquakes are the inevitable product of a dynamic planet – as the tectonic plates float around on a vast ocean of magma, slipping over, under and against each other, they produce energy of unimaginable proportions that can cause anything from an unnoticeable jiggle to an apocalyptic tsunami.

Although earthquakes can happen anywhere – the UK, hundreds of miles from any fault line, experiences more than 300 every year, mostly too small to notice – around 95% of the world's earthquakes occur along the borders between two plates. When these plates move against each other, stress builds up until the pressure becomes too great and they snap free of each other, creating a sudden jolt felt on the ground as an earthquake.

The near-chaotic behaviour of an earthquake makes it almost impossible to predict, however the largest earthquakes tend to be preceded by foreshocks – mini-quakes that are a sign of intense pressure building up – minutes before the earthquake proper is unleashed. We can make vague predictions – for example, the United States Geological Survey (USGS) has stated that there is a 67% chance of a massive earthquake in San Francisco in the next 30 years – but accurate prediction technology looks to be some way off. The best defence technique we have, therefore, is simply hiding out in earthquake-proof buildings built with super-strong materials that can bend, stretch and compress without breaking while the world literally falls apart around us.

Six folk tales explaining earthquakes

Assam, India A race of people live inside the Earth shake the ground from time to time to find out if anyone is still living on the surface above. During earthquakes, the local children shout 'Alive! Alive!' to tell their subterranean cousins they're still alive and well.

Kamchatka, Siberia The great god Tuli drives the Earth around the cosmos on a gigantic sled. The flea-infested dogs that smoothly pull the sled along occasionally have to stop to scratch, shaking the Earth in the process.

West Africa The Earth is flat, held up on one side by a huge mountain and on the other by a powerful giant, whose wife holds up the sky. Every so often the giant is overcome with romance, and while 'hugging' his wife the Earth trembles uncontrollably.

New Zealand The earthquake god Ru, son of the Earth and the Sky gods Papa and Rangi, is held within the Earth's 'womb', deep below the surface. When he stretches and kicks, the ground above shakes.

Central America Four gods stand at each corner of a flat, square Earth. If they all agree that the Earth above them is becoming overpopulated, they tip it to get rid of the surplus.

Scandinavia The writhing of the god Loki (pictured) as he is punished in an underground cave for the murder of his brother Baldur causes the Earth to shake violently. A serpent drips venom on him while his wife Sigyn sits beside him collecting it in a bowl. Every time the bowl is full she must go and empty it, and as the venom hits Loki's face he writhes, causing an earthquake.

On shaky ground

How earthquakes are measured

Despite the fact that the almost obligatory Richter-scale figure is rolled out during any news report on an earthquake, scientists haven't actually used the scale for more than 30 years. The number we're given refers to the Moment Magnitude Scale, which was developed in 1977 by Hiroo Kanamori. It is perhaps a testament to the influence of Charles Richter – and the tongue-twisting torpor of Kanamori's title – that the name for the pioneering seismologist's scale has stuck.

Seismographs have been around for nearly 2,000 years. Chang Heng, a Chinese astronomer, is thought to have invented the first makeshift seismoscope in 132AD by placing a pendulum inside a jar surrounded by eight bronze dragon heads, each holding a ball in its mouth. During an earthquake, the pendulum would swing away from the seismic waves, knocking the ball out of one of the dragon's jaws and showing from which direction the earthquake was coming.

By Richter's time, seismographs had improved a little but still only measured movement through a pen held still while the ground moved – and there was no universally accepted way of measuring what these seismographs actually recorded. With his 1935 scale, Richter simplified everything: he used one standard instrument (the Wood-Anderson seismograph), measured only nearby earthquakes in Southern California, and took only one piece of data – the distance the pen moved up and down – and applied it to a simple mathematical formula. However there was always the niggling problem of 'saturation': earthquakes above a magnitude of 8.0 tended to become muddled together as the pen went into a frenzy. The Chile earthquake of 1960, the largest ever recorded, reached just 8.5 on the Richter scale, although we now know it was a 9.5.

Kanamori's scale overcame this problem by not using seismometer readings at all, but rather by employing complex mathematics to find the total energy released in a quake. As a rough guide, a 5.0 earthquake releases around the same amount of energy as 32 kilotons of TNT, or the equivalent of the atomic bomb that exploded over Nagasaki. Chile's 9.5 earthquake was equivalent to 178 gigatons, or 5.5 million nuclear bombs.

The Modified Mercalli scale

While the Richter scale offers a quantifiable measure of an earthquake's magnitude, the Modified Mercalli scale (developed by Giuseppi Mercalli in 1883 and later built upon by others) concentrates on its intensity and the damage it causes. The differences between the two scales are summed up in the measurements they offer of the San Francisco earthquake of 1906: it measured 7.7 to 7.9 on the Richter scale (by no means devastating), but in some areas it reached at least X on the Modified Mercalli scale – a testament to the extensive damage it caused.

I Instrumental	Not felt except by a very few under especially favourable conditions
II Feeble	Felt only by a few people, especially on upper floors of buildings. Delicately suspended objects may swing
III Slight	Felt quite noticeably by people indoors, especially on upper floors of buildings. Many do not recognise it as an earthquake. Parked cars may rock slightly. Vibration similar to that caused by a passing truck
IV Moderate	Felt indoors by many, outdoors by few during the day. At night, some awakened. Dishes, windows, doors disturbed; walls make a cracking sound. Sensation like a heavy truck striking a building. Parked cars noticeably rocked
V Slightly strong	Felt by nearly everyone; many awakened. Some dishes and windows broken. Unstable objects overturned. Pendulum clocks may stop
VI Strong	Felt by all, many frightened. Windows broken; some heavy furniture moved; a few instances of fallen plaster. Damage slight
VII Very strong	Difficult to stand. Damage negligible in buildings of good design and construction; slight to moderate damage in well-built structures; considerable damage in poorly built or badly designed structures; some chimneys broken. Noticed by people driving cars
VIII Destructive	Damage slight in specially designed structures; considerable damage in ordinary substantial buildings with partial collapse. Damage great in poorly built structures. Fall of chimneys, factory stacks, columns, monuments, walls. Heavy furniture moved
IX Ruinous	Damage considerable in specially designed structures; well-designed frame structures thrown out of plumb. Damage great in substantial buildings, with partial collapse. Buildings shifted off foundations
X Disastrous	Some well-built wooden structures destroyed; most masonry and frame structures destroyed, along with foundations. Rails bent
XI Very disastrous	Few if any masonry structures remain standing. Bridges destroyed. Rails bent greatly
XII Catastrophic	Total damage. Ground rises and falls in waves. Objects thrown into the air. Large amounts of rock may move

James Hansen
(b. 29 March 1941)
American climatologist

James Hansen has been a thorn in the side of governments and global-warming sceptics for more than two decades. Head of Nasa's Goddard Institute for Space Studies (GISS), he has become the most influential scientist in the field of climate change, often suffering personal attack and censorship because of his views – he has even earned the epithet 'the most famous "silenced" scientist since Galileo'. The fact that global warming has become a household term can largely be put down to this crusading environmentalist.

> 66 *We never know the worth of water till the well is dry.*
>
> Thomas Fuller

Hansen became involved in the field in the mid-Seventies, when research into climate change was still in its infancy. In 1976 he calculated the impact man-made gases might have on the Earth, making the potential for catastrophe clear; in 1978, the US Congress passed the National Climate Program Act, establishing a small government office dedicated to researching the issue.

However, in 1981 Ronald Reagan came to power and all environmental departments found their budgets slashed. In the same year Hansen published a report stating that climate change was very real and would soon lead to a potentially lethal rise in global temperatures. The story made the front page of the *New York Times*, and the Department of Energy quickly halted the upstart's funding. Hansen continued his work quietly at GISS until in 1988 he was called before the Senate, under pressure from a young Al Gore, to reveal his findings. His testimony – that not only is the Earth's atmosphere warming up, but also that it is our fault – sent ripples through Washington. The first Bush administration complained to Nasa, and Hansen's theories were ridiculed in Congress. But 20 years on, climate change is now seen as an urgent threat.

Bird's-eye view

Google Earth's mapping of the planet

For more than three years, computer users have been able to travel the world instantly, using satellite imagery to swoop over mountains, valleys, cities and villages in increasingly impressive detail. The ambitious venture began at Keyhole, a tiny Silicon Valley software company which launched EarthViewer in 2001. During the early stages of the Iraq war the press jumped on this video game-influenced innovation, using it to simulate flying over Baghdad, and EarthViewer's ensuing popularity caught the eye of Google, which quietly snapped up the company in 2004. Within a year the redeveloped programme was freely available to the masses, restyled as Google Earth, and has since been downloaded 350 million times worldwide.

The programme is a patchwork of thousands of images taken by aerial photographers and a number of satellites, including several licensed from Nasa. Because a variety of sources are used to create this global jigsaw, Google Earth's accuracy can easily range from the highest resolution (you can pick out soft-drink cans lying on Las Vegas streets) to the very lowest (the Scilly Isles, 16 sq km in size, are little more than a blur), and some of the pictures can be at least five years old.

That is not to say that Google Earth's minor inadequacies have let it escape the issues facing all freely available programmes using satellite technology (Microsoft's Virtual Earth and Nasa's World Wind being two major competitors) – namely privacy and the little matter of national security. In 2006 one eagle-eyed user discovered a strange topographical feature deep in the Chinese wilderness. In the middle of an arid plain, what seemed like man-made mountain peaks, glacial lakes and snowdrifts sat alongside a military installation. It soon became perfectly clear to the Indian authorities that the Chinese army had built a small-scale replica of the border zone Aksai Chin, an area which has been a bone of contention for China and India since they went to war over the mountainous territory in 1962. Google has agreed to blur several key military and political sites, but North Korean nuclear reactors, Chinese submarines and even the infamous Area 51 are all still clearly visible.

Just deserts

The shifting sands of the world's arid regions

Deserts cover an astonishing 20% of the globe, and although the archetypal desert is hot, dry and sandy, it can also be cold and even snow-covered, without a sand dune in sight. In 1953 American geographer Peveril Meigs subdivided the world's desert regions into three categories. He recognised that there were extremely arid lands with at least 12 consecutive months without precipitation and arid areas with an average annual rainfall of less than 250mm. These he called deserts. Areas of semi-arid grassland, which receive between 250 and 500mm of precipitation a year, he then referred to as steppes.

The majority of deserts form at the point at which low rainfall kills off plant life, exposing the Earth's surface to the ravages of wind and erosion processes. Lighter topsoils are slowly blown away, exposing the heavier rock layers beneath them. The desert atmosphere contains very little humidity, so the Sun's rays are unimpeded and heat up the ground during the day. At night, however, deserts can become extremely cold, and this huge difference in temperatures – the diurnal range – results in severe weathering of the rock. Cold deserts form near the poles, where there is very little heat or rainfall but there are snowy winters. Coastal deserts, such as Chile's Atacama, tend to be cold because of the effect of neighbouring cold ocean currents, which cool the air blowing over the arid land.

What's the story behind oases?

Islands of abundant life in an ocean of intemperate (or extreme) desert wasteland, oases are formed at points in a desert where the land dips to a point just above the water table. This allows springs to form, harnessing water reserves built up from the sparse rainfall that will occasionally visit even the driest desert – and from these springs life can flourish. The largest oasis in the world, the Kharga in the Egyptian Sahara, is more than 100 miles long and was formed by heavy wind erosion, which caused the shifting sand (technically sand is any granular material between 2mm and 0.06mm in diameter) on the desert's surface to be swept aside, allowing the development of lush growth.

Singing sand

Marco Polo described their eerie sounds as 'spirit voices', while English desert-explorer RA Bagnold likened them to 'sirens who lure travellers to a waterless doom' and described them as a 'quite musical, pleasing, rhythmic sound of astonishing depth'. 'Booming' sand dunes can be found in only 30 locations around the world, where sand avalanches cause sounds variously described as roaring, booming, singing and even musical. These rare granular crooners are more homogeneous and more rounded than their mute counterparts, so as an avalanche pours down a dune, the grains of sand vibrate, creating voluminous noises. Recent studies have shown that it takes a layer of sand only a few grains thick to produce sounds as loud as 110 decibels (around the same sonic intensity as a rock concert), therefore just slipping down a steep dune, ankle-deep in the sand, should be enough to produce a sound similar to that of a B-29 bomber.

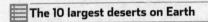

The 10 largest deserts on Earth

	Desert	Country or region	Size in square miles
1	Sahara	Africa	3,320,000
2	Arabian	Saudi Arabia	900,000
3	Gobi	China	500,000
4	Patagonian	Argentina	260,000
5	Rub' al-Khali	Middle East	250,000
6	Great Victoria	Australia	250,000
7	Kalahari	Africa	225,000
8	Great Basin	Nevada, USA	190,000
9	Chihuahuan	Mexico	175,000
10	Thar	India/Pakistan	175,000

Michael Benton

Apart from getting a dinosaur book when I was seven, one of the main things that motivated me to become a palaeontologist was the desire to understand how the world got to be the way it is today. I find the 'tree of life' concept fascinating – that you can link all organisms, living and extinct. Life didn't originate all over the place in a scatter-gun way. There was a history, and we can study that history.

It's an exciting time to be a palaeontologist. We now have the computing power to fill in a lot of the gaps in our knowledge of the ancient world. To what extent can we use clever analytical techniques to test ideas about what ancient organisms might have been like? People will look at *Jurassic Park* and say: 'That's just imagination' – but you can figure out a great deal: whether an animal ran on two legs or ate meat, or what its maximum bite-force was. You don't need a time machine. Although there are of course certain things you can't know for sure – what colour a creature was, for instance.

At the moment I'm focusing on the Permian and Triassic periods, 200-300 million years ago, before the dinosaurs came on the scene. I'm particularly interested in this episode because it's when the first quite complex ecosystems of vertebrates became established on land. It's also when the biggest-ever mass extinction occurred, wiping out 90% or more of the species on Earth. A major cause, we think, was a series of massive volcanic eruptions. It took 25m years for the complexity to re-evolve, at which point the dinosaurs appeared.

My study of the period means I've been doing a lot of fieldwork in Russia, on the Permo-Triassic boundary in the Ural Mountain area. We're looking at detrital deposits on riverbeds, where you find a great abundance of broken-up bone fragments and teeth and scales. Chasing whole dinosaur specimens is great, but museums are full of them and they rarely give you new information. The detrital stuff is less sexy, but it can tell you what you want to know about the whole fauna – about all the creatures that lived together in this one spot.

It's not always fragments, though. One of my best experiences was when I was a student working in the Canadian badlands. We were out in well-known dino territory and I found a Hadrosaur, a duck-billed dinosaur. It took us two weeks to clear the rock, starting in the belly region and moving out to the legs and tail. Then we followed the other way, asking ourselves: 'Will there be skull?' We got to the end of the neck and... no, there wasn't. It had broken off and been washed away. But it was very exciting all the same.

The Midwestern United States has yielded hundreds of specimens, because the terrain makes them accessible and thousands of people over there are desperately excited about dinosaurs. But they don't find a lot of species these days. The hotspots at the moment are parts of China, Mongolia and Africa. In these less exploited areas you're more likely to find something new.

We are aware of a lot of fossils, but we don't know how many gaps there are in our picture of the tree of life. It's an interesting question: how complete is our knowledge of the fauna from any time slice in the past? It's not that bad is the general conclusion.

Our knowledge of the past can be used to help us understand what might happen in the future. In reconstructing the tree of life and studying mass extinctions, you realise that a lot of the species we have today will become extinct. We can't save them all, so it's important to ask which ones should be given priority. We need to preserve the largest genetic diversity possible. You look for living organisms that don't have any close living relatives, such as the panda. There is nothing else like it on Earth, whereas it would be less serious if we lost a species of lizard or stick insect. It sounds awful, but you need to be rational in order to be useful. It doesn't mean we don't care.

Will humans go the way of the dinosaurs? Probably not. We have the biological hallmarks of a successful species: we are abundant, widespread and have diverse diets – and of course we have consciousness. The poor old panda is on the other end of the scale. **MICHAEL BENTON**

Michael Benton is professor of vertebrate palaeontology at the University of Bristol and was an adviser on the BBC's Walking With Dinosaurs *series*

A fossil

There are two major types of fossil: body fossils and trace fossils. Body fossils are parts of an animal or plant – the bones, teeth, or leaves. Trace fossils are records of a creature's movements and activities, such as fossilised footprints and dung.

Organic matter from dead animals and plants is covered rapidly in sediment – either silt and mud under water, or sand or volcanic ash above ground – or coated in tar or tree sap and preserved. Over time, the surrounding sediment is compressed by further layers of material and hardens into sedimentary rock such as sandstone, siltstone, shale and limestone. The skeleton, shell, branch or leaf is trapped and over time dissolves in ground water, leaving a cavity which in turn is filled with mineral deposits to produce a perfect cast of the original bone or leaf. Erosion then wears down the surrounding rock until the fossil is exposed in a riverbed or cliff face. In fact, the word fossil comes from the Latin *fossilis*, meaning 'dug up' and originally meant anything taken from the Earth. It wasn't until the 19th century that the word came to specifically mean traces of life in rocks.

The oldest fossils date back around 3,500 million years, and their age is ascertained by looking at where they were found and working out their age relative to the surrounding rock and through the more complex process of absolute radiometric dating, which measures the radioactive decay of elements in the rock. Some of the most well-known fossils besides dinosaurs are the trilobites (pictured) – funny-looking ancient marine creatures whose bodies ranged from a couple of millimetres to almost a metre in length and which died out around 250m years ago. Some of the most famous British examples were found in the limestone mines of Dudley in the West Midlands, where they were known as the Dudley Bug and even appear on the town's coat of arms.

✳ Michael Benton's guide to finding a dinosaur

It's not like *Jurassic Park*, where you give a few flicks of the brush and a beautiful skeleton turns up. Go to a place where the rock is the right age and there's evidence that stuff has been found in the past, and walk up and down likely spots where there is a reasonable amount of erosion going on. The North American badlands and the steppes in Russia are good because they're both quite bare and there are ravines where the water has washed away the soil. March up and down, and don't stop to hammer until you see bits of bone. Follow the scraps of bone back up the side of the ravine, and if you're lucky you may spot the layer where they're coming from. If you're luckier still, you might have the outline of a complete specimen peeping out at you. It usually takes at least two or three weeks to get right down to the fossil and extract it. Here are five key finds...

1 Megalosaurus, Oxfordshire, UK (1824) William Buckland discovered fragments of a Megalosaurus ('great lizard') in 1824. It was the first dinosaur to be named before the word dinosaur had even been coined.

2 Hadrosaurus, Haddonfield, New Jersey, US (1858) The first complete skeleton of a dinosaur discovered in America, from which people learned for the first time that some dinosaurs were bipedal.

3 Archaeopteryx, Bavaria, Germany (1860) The first fossil of an early bird – a missing link – to be found, coincidentally very soon after the publication of Darwin's *Origin of Species*. It's not a dinosaur in the classic sense, but the Archaeopteryx has iconic status.

4 Protoceratops, Gobi Desert, Mongolia (1922) The first discovery, by Roy Chapman Andrews' expedition, of a nest containing dinosaur eggs with embryos inside them, as well as an abundance of Protoceratops remains.

5 Deinonychus, Montana, US (1964) John Ostrom's discovery in Montana of a Deinonychus – which could leap through the air and rip at its prey with its enormous slashing claws – gave rise to the popular modern conception of dinosaurs as dynamic, warm-blooded creatures. **MICHAEL BENTON**

Sounding out

How the depths of the oceans are fathomed

Before the First World War, ocean depths were determined by a method known as lead-line sounding. A rope with a weight attached is lowered to the sea floor until the line goes slack, then the weight is pulled back up and the distance from the surface mark to the weight is measured. The depth is usually given in fathoms, a word derived from the Old English *fæðm*, meaning 'a pair of outstretched arms' and which equates to 1.83m (6ft). On board ships, a sailor would measure the depth by running the rope between his outstretched hands and counting the number of spans, or fathoms.

> ❝ It is of great use to the sailor to know the length of his line, though he cannot with it fathom all the depths of the ocean.
>
> John Locke

This method is obviously rather time consuming, and so during the war underwater sound technology was developed to help submarines detect submerged targets – and sonar was born, changing the way the sea floor was mapped. After the war, the sonic depth finder, or echo sounder, was developed to help determine the depth of water – not simply the distance to a target – by measuring the time it takes a sound, or sonic pulse, produced just below the surface to echo back from the seabed. In shallow water the sound waves will return very fast, and in deeper water it will take more time to receive the echoes. The depth of the ocean is then calculated by multiplying the time it takes for the echo to return by the speed with which sound travels through sea water – approximately 1,500 metres per second.

The Earth's five oceans

Pacific	69,375,000 sq miles
Atlantic	41,105,000 sq miles
Indian	28,900,000 sq miles
Antarctic (Southern)	7,848,000 sq miles
Arctic	5,440,000 sq miles

Blue planet

The world's seas and oceans

From space, the importance of water to our planet is crystal clear. The Earth's surface is in fact 71% water, covering around 140 million square miles (361m sq km), but this vast reservoir has changed in size over the planet's lifetime – the water has for periods been locked up in ice covering much of the globe. However, just 2% of the world's water is fresh; the rest is salty, with around 3.5% salinity.

> 66 *The sea, once it casts its spell, holds one in its net of wonder forever.*
> Jacques Yves Cousteau

The difference between an ocean, a sea and a lake can often be slight and it is down to the International Hydrographic Organization, founded in 1921 and the last word in defining bodies of water and their boundaries, to make the distinction. There is one World Ocean which contains all the free-flowing interconnected bodies of water on the Earth's surface that are not landlocked. Within this vast expanse of water are five oceans: the Arctic, Antarctic (or Southern), Atlantic, Indian and Pacific. And then within these oceans are smaller seas which are delimited by their geographical situation – either because they are landlocked saline bodies, are defined by an archipelago or are connected to the ocean through a small channel (as with the Mediterranean).

Sea change: five misnamed bodies of water

Sea of Galilee In fact it's a small freshwater lake called Lake Tiberias

Sea of Cortés Actually known as the Gulf of California

Dead Sea It's not a sea – it's a very salty lake

Caspian Sea Another lake – the largest in the world

Persian Gulf This one goes the other way – it is in fact a sea

Wading in...

Five sacred rivers and the threats they face

1 The Nile

No river matches the mystery and romance of the Nile, at least not since the rediscovery of ancient Egypt and its capture of the public imagination (and millions of tourists). As Egypt's life depended absolutely on the Nile and its annual flood, it's no surprise that the river was revered for having divine origins. The Nile's genesis lay in a tangle of myths involving divinities like Khnum, the creator, and Osiris, the redeemer. The god of the Nile itself was the surprisingly gnomic Hapi, a cheery old man with pendulous breasts and belly, sprouting vegetation – the original Old Man River. Like other civilisations, Egypt saw the Milky Way as a celestial counterpart of the Nile – as above, so below. The major part of the Nile's 4,200-mile course, south of Aswan, was little known to Ancient Egypt: not until 2006 was its entire length navigated – a feat recorded in the IMAX film *Mystery of the Nile*.

2 The Ganges

The holiest of India's rivers, the Ganges is personified as Ma Ganga, the goddess of life-giving waters. The World Wildlife Fund estimates that one in every 12 humans in the world still depends on the river for their livelihood via agriculture and fishing. Hindu spiritual life has always been entwined with the Ganges – numerous temples lay along its banks, notably at Varanasi, also a favoured place for cremation and the disposal of ashes, 'crossing over' the river of life. Along the Ganges' 1,500 miles are numerous other *tirthas*, where people bathe in the saving waters to salve their souls. The Ganges has a high oxygen count but its resilience is being tested by widespread pollution and waterborne disease, while a new UN report suggests that climate change may destroy the Himalayan glaciers that feed the Ganges by 2030. Oh Ma.

3 The Jordan

What it lacks in grandeur and length (it's a mere 156 miles) the Jordan makes up for in history and myth. The Old Testament describes it as nourishing 'the gardens of God' and recounts the Israelites, bearing the ark of the covenant, crossing it while its waters 'rose in one heap'. In song and sermon 'crossing the Jordan' became a metaphor for deliverance, perhaps from life itself. It was in Jordan's waters that John the Baptist operated, baptising Jesus there. The upper sections of the river still see baptisms, but below the Sea of Galilee the Jordan has become a sewage-laden stream, its flow drastically depleted by irrigation and use as drinking water, with its ecosystem now listed by Friends of the Earth as one of the world's 100 most endangered sites.

4 The Thames

Not always thought of as holy waters, and modestly endowed with awesome features, the Thames was clearly reckoned sacred by ancient Britain. Its 215 miles have delivered many Bronze and Iron Age treasures deposited as votive offerings, among them the Battersea shield (found in 1857). In 2007 writer Peter Ackroyd reclaimed its sanctity in his psychogeographical history *Thames: Sacred River*. Between times the Thames has been more about commerce than piety, and its long-term pollution hit crisis point with the Great Stink of 1858, which resulted in the construction of London's sewage system. These days salmon leap from its silvery waters (if you look long enough), proving that Old Father Thames is at least halfway towards godliness.

5 The Stikine, Seena and Nass

They may not be international names, but these are among the most important salmon rivers in Canada, and this trio is held sacred by the indigenous Tahltan First Nation. Since 2005 the rivers' Sacred Headwaters, which lie in a valley in the wilderness of British Columbia, have been the site of a standoff between the Tahltan people and Royal Dutch Shell, which plans to extract methane gas from the valley, a process which involves pumping hundreds of thousands of tons of chemical-laden water into coalbeds – and then pumping the toxic effluent into any nearby rivers. With several hundred wells and 1m acres involved, the stakes are high. In December 2007 Shell lost a second high court injunction against the Tahltan, who have been doggedly blocking access to their land. Here's where Canada decides what's sacred – rivers or money. NEIL SPENCER

Après le déluge...

The history of the Earth's tumultuous floods

Noah's legendary flood is merely a drop in the ocean of flood myths which have made an appearance in a substantial proportion of the world's religions and belief systems throughout history. Hundreds of civilisations, from the Greeks to the Aztecs to the Hindus, have told strikingly similar stories of a deity, wary of man, bringing a great deluge upon the Earth and in the process wiping out all of humanity, save a select few.

The Ancient Sumerians wrote that the immortal king Ziusudra was warned by the gods of a great flood, and told to build a boat to weather the storm. This myth passed through subsequent Mesopotamian civilisations (centred around modern-day Iraq, in between the Tigris and Euphrates rivers), until by the time of the *Epic of Gilgamesh* (a poem written between 1300-1000BC) the boat had become a huge ark which could carry 'the seed of all living creatures', while the flood encompassed the whole globe apart from the top of the mountain Nisur, where the ark landed. This tale passed into the neighbouring Hebrew lands, finally washing up in the Book of Genesis, with Noah substituted for the immortal Babylonian Utnapishtim, and Mount Ararat for Nisur.

Historians and geologists alike have speculated for decades on these watery myths. Tsunamis, meteor impacts and the excessive flooding of riverine flood plains have all been proffered as causes – and one recent theory suggests that a deluge of water flowing into the Black Sea from the Mediterranean in 5600BC caused the sea level to rise by several hundred feet, triggering mass migrations across Europe and the Middle East, particularly into Mesopotamia. However, these tend to be localised theories which don't explain how isolated civilisations, such as the Polynesians in the Pacific or the Aborigines in Australia, share the same myths. More than 10,000 years ago, as warmer weather began to replace the last ice age (or glaciation), melting glaciers would have caused sea levels to rise by up to 120m, wiping out thousands of species and dramatically altering the world's coastlines. Could oral tradition have preserved this cataclysmic event in the form of a mythical flood?

Five flood myths

Judaeo-Christian God, wishing to punish humanity for its sinfulness, warned Noah, a righteous 600-year-old, that he was going to unleash a great deluge upon the Earth, and gave him specific instructions to build an ark big enough to hold two of every living creature. The waters came and inundated the Earth for 150 days before slowly receding, at which point Noah rested the ark on the peak of Mount Ararat. After it was over, God vowed never to flood the Earth again.

Australian Aboriginal Long ago a huge frog drank all the world's water, causing a global drought. All the animals in Australia eventually gathered together and resolved to make the frog laugh and spit the water back out in the process. An eel eventually managed it by wriggling and flopping about, hugely entertaining the frog, from whom all the water poured. The water quickly filled the Earth, reaching the peaks of the highest mountains, and causing many humans and animals to drown.

Hindu Manu, the first human, saved a tiny fish from the jaws of a larger one while washing his hands in a river. The fish, thankful for Manu's kindness, returned to warn him of a great impending flood. So Manu then built a huge boat and filled it with samples of every species, which the fish towed to a mountaintop, where it was safe from the deluge.

Norse When Ymir, the first giant, was murdered by the god Odin he collapsed, and so much blood poured from his body that it drowned the entire race of giants, save for the frost giant Bergelmir and his wife. They escaped on a ship and began a new race of giants, while Ymir's body was used to form the Earth, and his blood the seas.

Mayan After the first attempts by the creator god, or Feathered Serpent, at making man from mud failed, he discovered that his second attempt – using wood this time – was also flawed because his creations' lack of a heart, mind or soul meant they couldn't worship him. To destroy his botched men, the god sent a flood which killed all but a few of his creations, who escaped and over the ages became monkeys.

James Lovelock

I first developed the Gaia hypothesis in 1965, when I was designing instruments at the Jet Propulsion Laboratories in California. Nasa asked me to be an experimenter on their lunar and planetary missions because they needed the kind of instruments I made to analyse the surface and atmosphere of the planets.

I started talking with the biologists at Nasa about a mission they were planning to send to Mars. We argued about the best way of detecting the existence of life on the planet. It occurred to me that rather than scooping up some soil and growing the organisms you might find in it, you could simply analyse the composition of the planet's atmosphere. If there was no life, the gases in the atmosphere would have reached equilibrium. If life did exist, it would be using the atmosphere to get its raw materials and dump its waste products, just like we do – and that would show up in chemical analysis.

These thoughts led me to look more closely at our own planet, and when I did, it became more and more extraordinary to me that we have reactive gases such as methane and oxygen co-existing. How could they possibly stay constant in composition for long periods of time unless something was regulating the whole process?

Then an astronomer asked me if I knew that the Sun has warmed up by about 30% since life began. So why, if it was warm enough when it started, haven't we completely fried since? And if it is warm enough now, why wasn't it frozen solid back then? It suddenly dawned on me: if life can regulate the atmosphere, it can regulate the climate. That gave birth to the Gaia hypothesis: that the biosphere regulates the atmosphere and surface of the Earth so as to keep it habitable.

Biologists vigorously attacked the hypothesis because they thought it was anti-Darwinian and a new form of creationism. But gradually evidence came in from the Earth that there were indeed systems regulating climate and chemistry, both in the ocean and on the land. It took until 2001 for scientists to come out and say it, but they wouldn't use the word Gaia: they called it Earth Systems Science.

The Earth has lived a remarkably long time, between a quarter and a third of the age of the universe, which is longer than many suns have lived. It has withstood all kinds of perturbations and disturbances, and what we're doing to it now is relatively mild by comparison. The earth looks after itself, and if we upset it, it self-regulates – and it looks like it's doing so by trying to eliminate us.

If we don't begin to understand the Earth we live on, we're going to make an awful mess in trying to cure the problem that faces us in the coming century. There is not a lot we can do now to stop it heating up – it's probably too late. The way things look, anything up to 80% of the present population will no longer be with us by the end of the century. So we've got to prepare for some pretty huge changes.

Understanding what will happen, where it's going to be good to live and what to do – this is going to take up all our energy. It's important not to aim for pointless things such as sustainable development. There are just too many people, more than the Earth can carry.

I could be wrong. Natural events or some very clever idea could change things. There's talk of putting an aerosol in the stratosphere that would reflect sunlight and cool the Earth. That's not a bad idea, but it's just like going on a dialysis machine when your kidneys fail. It can buy you some time. And if the alternative is death, who wouldn't take it? I don't think we'll disappear entirely. Our danger is being reduced to a Stone Age of warlords and all the rest, like when the Roman civilisation broke up. Our job is to carry on the message of civilisation until things stabilise.

We are part of Gaia. There have always been organisms that come along and change the whole scene and they have always brought as many disadvantages with them as advantages. But the system finally settles out and makes use of the benefits. I think the same is true of us. We've done an immense amount of damage to the planet, but it would be appalling from Gaia's point of view to lose us. We are also a great benefit. It's a matter of reaching an equilibrium. **JAMES LOVELOCK**

Dr James Lovelock is the author of the groundbreaking Gaia: A New Look at Life on Earth *published in 1979 and the recent follow-up* The Revenge of Gaia: Why the Earth Is Fighting Back – And How We Can Still Save Humanity

Our geological footprint

The effect mankind has had on the Earth

The idea of an Anthropocene epoch isn't new. People have suggested for more than a century that humans have altered the Earth, but the idea was crystallised by Paul Crutzen, the Nobel prize-winning chemist, in 2002, in the journal *Nature*. He said that humans have impacted so severely on the Earth's atmosphere, oceans, biota and landscape that we're now in an interval dominated by human, rather than natural, forces. The term began to be used in books and scientific papers, yet it still hadn't been formally examined by geologists. So we (members of the Stratigraphy Commission of the Geological Society of London) examined whether the Anthropocene should really become part of the geological time-scale. Our proposal's now been published: the Anthropocene does seem geologically real and could be judged to have begun in 1800. The International Commission on Stratigraphy must now decide whether our argument is correct and helpful scientifically. Geologists are rather conservative as regards the time-scale, so to adopt this change would be a big step.

The acid test is whether today's changes will translate into future geology. By comparing with the past, we can estimate what today's global changes might mean in the long run. We also have to be precise about the scale of this time-span. Should the Anthropocene be an epoch, like the modern Holocene? Or a period, such as the Jurassic? Or even an era, which could last for hundreds of millions of years? The evidence now suggests the Anthropocene as an epoch, but should it become an era, the future is indeed uncertain. Humans have taken this enormously complicated Earth machine of interrelated land, oceans, atmospheres and biota and hit it hard. How it's going to evolve is still unclear. If we have done enough to derail the next few ice advances, we could be ending the Quaternary period. Given the extinction event that's developing and our distinctive geochemical signals, this new interval of time could be big. It's still early days – we're only a couple of centuries in. The Holocene epoch (the last 11,000 years) has been very stable. Temperature and sea level, once stabilised, have barely budged, which has allowed human civilisation to flourish. This stability won't last.

We can see a possible future Earth by searching in its history. About 55 million years ago, in the Eocene epoch, and 185m years ago, in the Toarcian age of the Jurassic period, there were large influxes of carbon into the atmosphere. Each time, global temperatures rose by 5C to 7C globally, and there were extinction events and changes in ocean circulation. The Earth then took more than 100,000 years to recover. We haven't put quite so much carbon into the atmosphere yet, but today levels of carbon dioxide are rising much faster. Over the last 200 years we've taken much of the world's carbon stocks – a good few hundred million years' worth – and put them into the atmosphere. That's geologically remarkable, and will undoubtedly have an effect.

We know some of the likely effects. Sea level is set to rise significantly. For every one-degree rise in global temperature, a 10-20m rise may occur over the coming millennia. Acidification of the oceans brought about by carbon dioxide dissolving in them – it's already happening – will leave permanent evidence. Coral reefs, to a geologist, are not just wonderful ecosystems to swim past: they are magnificent rock-producing structures. Now they're being hit by the quadruple whammy of rising acidity and temperatures, pollution and the decimation of reef fish. Kill off the reefs, and you kill off part of the geological record. Humans will leave other geological footprints. A city is, in a way, a massive rock stratum, for concrete is as durable stuff as you can find in geology. There might not, though, be much fossil fuel in the future. Once our coal and oil supplies run out, it will take many millions of years for the Earth to replenish them.

So can we do anything to cut short the Anthropocene? Our impact now seems indelible, and we're not yet doing much to halt the changes. Taking carbon out of the atmosphere and putting it underground would need an enormous global effort, but might help stop the Anthropocene from turning into a geological period – or even an era. Unless this global effort comes soon, we'll lose our Eden forever. **DR JAN ZALASIEWICZ**

Dr Jan Zalasiewicz chairs the Stratigraphy Commission of the Geological Society of London, and is a geology lecturer at the University of Leicester

Looking forward

What the future holds for the Earth

Geologists have a notoriously hard time predicting the Earth's future. On the geological timescale 1,000 years is barely a blip, and the Earth's processes don't follow an easy-to-read pattern. The looming spectre of climate change, however, could cause changes that normally take hundreds of thousands of years to happen in a matter of centuries, making it vital that we try to work out what may be on the horizon...

In 100 years If global warming continues at its current rate (which many scientists predict it will), by 2100 CO_2 levels will have reached their highest point for 650,000 years, causing 20% to 30% of species to become extinct, more than a third of the planet's climate zones to radically change, and ocean pH levels to reach their lowest point in 20 million years, wiping out most shellfish. Droughts and forest fires will plague some areas, hurricanes and floods others.

In 1,000 years Unless a solution has been found for runaway climate change, temperatures will have risen by at least 15C, with most of London flooded thanks to a sea-level rise of 11 metres. The impact caused by the release of methane stores from the oceans and Siberia will also now become apparent, and could cause an unstoppable cycle of warming.

In 18,000 years The next glaciation period will set in as temperatures plummet and glaciers invade regions at high latitude. Climate change may severely impact this process, however, bringing this date much closer or putting it off indefinitely.

In 5m years The supercontinent cycle will continue its inexorable dance as the Earth's plates reconfigure. The Straits of Gibraltar will close, causing the Mediterranean to dry up. Meanwhile, Ethiopia will now be an island and Australia will be travelling northwards, sweeping up neighbouring Asian islands that get in its way.

In 250m years All the continents will now be one, forming a single supercontinent: Pangaea Ultima.

In 5 billion years The Sun will become a red dwarf and finally die, taking the Earth with it.